Sorting: Groups and Graphs

A unit of study for grades 2–3
from USED NUMBERS: REAL DATA IN THE CLASSROOM

Developed at Technical Education Research Centers and Lesley College

Susan Jo Russell and Rebecca B. Corwin

DALE SEYMOUR PUBLICATIONS

The *Used Numbers* materials were prepared with the support of National Science Foundation Grant No. MDR-8651649. Any opinions, findings, conclusions, or recommendations expressed in this publication are those of the authors and do not necessarily represent the views of the National Science Foundation. These materials shall be subject to a royalty-free, irrevocable, worldwide, nonexclusive license in the United States Government to reproduce, perform, translate, and otherwise use and to authorize others to use such materials for Government purposes.

Cover design and illustrations: Rachel Gage

Order number DS01036
ISBN 0-86651-515-1

DALE
SEYMOUR
PUBLICATIONS
P.O. BOX 10888
PALO ALTO, CA 94303

2 3 4 5 6 7 8 9 10 11-MA-95 94 93 92 91

USED NUMBERS STAFF

Co-principal investigators

Susan Jo Russell
Technical Education Research Centers (TERC)

Susan N. Friel
Lesley College

Curriculum development

Rebecca B. Corwin (TERC and Lesley College)
Tim Barclay (TERC)
Antonia Stone (Playing to Win)

Research and evaluation

Janice R. Mokros (TERC)
Alana Parkes (TERC)
Debra Gustafson (TERC)
John Olive (University of Georgia)
Deborah Ruff (University of Georgia)
Heide Wiegel (University of Georgia)
Bonnie Brownstein (Institute for Schools of the Future)
Ellen Bialo (Institute for Schools of the Future)
Michele Arsenault (Institute for Schools of the Future)
Mary Fullmer (University of Chicago)

Design and production

Elisabeth Roberts (TERC)
Jessica Goldberg (TERC)
LeAnn Davis (TERC)
John Abbe (TERC)
Laurie Aragon (COMAP)

Cooperating classrooms for this unit

Caroline Chin
Boston Public Schools

Sylvia Aquino
New York City Public Schools

Cathy Gruetter
Clarke County Public Schools, Georgia

Advisory board

Joan Akers, California State Department of Education
Bonnie Brownstein, Institute for Schools of the Future
James Landwehr, AT&T Bell Laboratories
Steven Leinwand, Connecticut State Department of Education
John Olive, University of Georgia
David Pillemer, Wellesley College
Andee Rubin, Bolt Beranek and Newman Laboratories
Cindy Stephens, D. C. Heath
Marion Walter, University of Oregon
Virginia Wooley, Boston Museum of Science

Thanks also to advice and comment from Marilyn Burns, Solomon A. Garfunkel (COMAP), and Bob Willcutt.

CONTENTS

PREFACE

In an information-rich society such as ours, statistics are an increasingly important aspect of daily life. We are constantly bombarded with information about everything around us. This wealth of data can become confusing, or it can help us make choices about our actions.

Educators and mathematicians now stress the importance of incorporating data analysis and statistics into the elementary mathematics curriculum to prepare students for living and working in a world filled with information based on data. The *Curriculum and Evaluation Standards for School Mathematics*, published by the National Council of Teachers of Mathematics in 1989, highlights statistics as one of the key content strands for all grade levels.

Many teachers see the need to support students in becoming better problem solvers in mathematics. However, it is difficult to find problems that give students the kind of experiences they need, are manageable in the classroom, and lead to the learning of essential mathematics. The area of data analysis—collecting, organizing, graphing, and interpreting data—provides a feasible, engaging context in which elementary grade students can do real mathematics. Students of all ages are interested in real data about themselves and the world around them.

Teaching statistics: Pedagogical issues

We introduce students to good literature in their early years. We do not reserve great literature until they are older—on the contrary, we encourage them to read it or we read it to them. Similarly, we can give young students experience with real mathematical processes rather than save the good mathematics for later.

Through collecting and analyzing real data, students encounter the uncertainty and intrigue of real mathematics. Mathematicians do not sit at desks doing isolated problems. Instead, they discuss, debate, and argue—building theories and collecting data to support them, working cooperatively (and sometimes competitively) to refine and develop such theories further.

Mathematicians and scientists use information or data like snapshots to look at, describe, and better understand the world. They cope with the real-world "messiness" of the data they encounter, which often do not lead to a single, clear answer.

Because statistics is an application of real mathematics skills, it provides the opportunity to model real mathematical behaviors. As students engage in the study of statistics, they, like scientists and statisticians, participate in:

▼ cooperative learning

▼ theory building

▼ discussing and defining terms and procedures

▼ working with messy data

▼ dealing with uncertainty

We want elementary school students to have the opportunity to engage in such real mathematical behavior, discussing, describing, challenging each other, and building theories about real-world phenomena based on their work.

Data analysis in the mathematics curriculum

Exploring data involves students directly in many aspects of mathematics. Data are collected through counting and measuring; they are sorted and classified; they are represented through graphs, pictures, tables, and charts. In summarizing and comparing data, students calculate, estimate, and choose appropriate units. In the primary grades, work with data is closely tied to the number relationships and measuring processes that students are learning. In the upper elementary grades, students encounter some of the approaches used in statistics for describing data and making inferences. Throughout the data analysis process, students make decisions about how to count and measure, what degree of accuracy is appropriate, and how much information is enough; they continually make connections between the numbers and what those numbers represent.

Instead of doing mathematics as an isolated set of skills unrelated to the world of reality, students can understand statistics as the vibrant study of the world in which they live, where numbers can tell them many different stories about aspects of their own lives. The computation they do is for a purpose, and the analysis they do helps them to understand how mathematics can function as a significant tool in describing, comparing, predicting, and making decisions. ■

TEACHING DATA ANALYSIS

The nature of data analysis

In data analysis, students use numbers to describe, compare, predict, and make decisions. When they analyze data, they search for patterns and attempt to understand what those patterns tell them about the phenomena the data represent.

A data analysis investigation generally includes recognizable phases:

▼ considering the problem

▼ collecting and recording data

▼ representing the data

▼ describing and interpreting the data

▼ developing hypotheses and theories based on the data

These phases often occur in a cycle: the development of a theory based on the data often leads to a new question, which may begin the data analysis cycle all over again.

Elementary students can collect, represent, and interpret real data. Although their work differs in many ways from that of adult statisticians, their processes are very similar. Elementary school students can both analyze data and use those data to describe and make decisions about real situations.

Because real data are the basis for investigations in data analysis, there are no predetermined "answers." For example, if your class collects data on the ages of the students' siblings, the students understand that their job is more than simply coming up with an answer that you knew all along. Not only do you *not* know the answer in advance, but, without seeing the data, you may not even know what the most interesting questions are going to be!

While this situation encourages students to do their own mathematical thinking, it can also feel risky for you. Many teachers welcome a little uncertainty in their mathematics classes, when it prods their students to be more independent thinkers. To support you, the authors provide sample experiences from teachers who have used the activities described here so that you can be prepared for the kinds of issues that are likely to arise. You will soon build your own repertoire of experiences with data analysis activities and will be able to anticipate likely questions, confusions, and opportunities.

The importance of discussion in mathematics

A central activity in data analysis is dialogue and discussion. While it is easy for you and your students to become engaged and enthusiastic in collecting data and making graphs, a significant amount of time should also be devoted to reflection about the meaning of the data.

Since students are not used to talking much during their mathematics work, it is important to support active decisionmaking by the students from the very beginning of the investigation. Students' participation in framing the initial question, choosing the methods of investigation, and deciding on ways to organize their data is essential. Once the data are collected and organized, the students must grapple with interpreting the results. If you have the outcome of a discussion or the "teaching points" you want to make too clearly in mind, you may guide students' observations too quickly into predetermined channels. When student ideas are ignored, misinterpreted, or rejected, they soon understand that their job is to second-guess the "answer" you had in mind.

On the other hand, if students find that *anything* they say is accepted in the same way, if every contribution is "a good idea" and no idea is ever challenged, they can lose motivation to participate. Ask students to reflect on, clarify, and extend their ideas and to listen to and ask questions of each other. Discussions in mathematics should encourage students to interpret numbers, make conjectures, develop theories, consider opposing views, and support their ideas with reasons.

Sensitive issues in data analysis

Students of all ages are interested in data about themselves and the issues they care about. Topics that matter enough to students to make them compelling topics for study often have very personal aspects. Investigations about families, heights, or students' chores, for example, can all bring up sensitive issues. After trying many topics in many classrooms, we have concluded that the potential sensitivity of a topic is not a reason to avoid it; on the contrary, these are the very topics that most engage student interest. All teachers deal with difficult or sensitive issues in their classroom, and the skills demanded of a teacher in handling issues that arise during data analysis activities are no different. Keep in mind that students may

sometimes want their data to be anonymous. Focusing on the patterns and shape of the class data, rather than on individual pieces of data, is particularly helpful, especially for upper elementary students.

Small-group work

Many of the investigations involve students working in teams. At first, keep small-group sessions short and focused. For students not used to working in small groups, assign specific tasks that encourage the participation of all the group members. For example, instead of, "Have a discussion in your group to decide what you want to ask the second graders about their bedtimes," you might say, "Come up with three possible questions you could ask the second graders."

Materials

Students need materials to represent their data during their investigations. These range from Unifix cubes to pencil and paper to computer software. What is most important is that students are able to construct multiple views of the data quickly and easily and that they do not become bogged down in drawing and coloring elaborate graphs (which are appropriate only at the very end of an investigation when students are ready to "publish" their findings).

Any material that can be moved easily and rearranged quickly offers possibilities for looking at data. For example, students might write or draw their data on *index*

cards (or any paper rectangles); then these can be arranged and rearranged. *Unifix cubes* (or other interconnecting cubes) are another good material for making representations throughout the grades. We have found that *stick-on notes* (such as Post-it notes), with each note representing one piece of data, are an excellent material for making rough drafts of graphs. They can be moved around easily and adhere to tables, desks, paper, or the chalkboard. *Pencil and unlined paper* should always be available for tallies, line plots, and other quick sketch graphs.

Calculators

Calculators should be available, if possible, throughout the activities. Their use is specifically suggested in some of the investigations. It is no secret to students that calculators are readily available in the world and that adults use them often. But many students do not know how to use a calculator accurately, do not check their results for reasonableness, and do not make sensible choices about when to use a calculator. Only through using calculators with appropriate guidance in the context of real problems can they gain these skills.

Computers

Computers are a key tool in data analysis in the world outside of school. Graphing software, for example, enables scientists and statisticians to display large sets of data quickly and to construct multiple views of the data easily. Some software for the elementary grades allows this flexibility as well. A finished graph made by the computer may, for some students, be an appropriate illustration for a final report of their findings. But keep in mind that students also make interesting and creative graphs by hand that would not be possible with the software available to them. Other computer software, including software for sorting and classifying and data base software, is particularly useful for some data analysis investigations. Where the use of a software tool would particularly enhance a data analysis investigation, recommendations for incorporating its use are made in the text and noted at the beginning of the session.

Home-school connections

Many opportunities arise in data analysis investigations for communicating with parents about the work going on in the classroom and for including them as participants in your data investigations. When you begin this unit, you may want to send a note home to parents explaining that students will be studying data analysis in their mathematics class and that, from time to time, parents can be of assistance in helping students collect data from home. Parents or other family members often provide an available comparison group. Studies of age, family size, height, and so forth can be extended to include parents. If students are studying their own families, they may be interested in collecting

comparison data about their parents' families. Including parents and other significant family members as participants in your data analysis investigations can stimulate their interest and enthusiasm for the work students are doing in school and, at the same time, help students see that the mathematics they do in school is connected to their life outside of school.

Interdisciplinary connections

Many teachers find ways to connect the data analysis experiences students have in mathematics to other areas of the curriculum. Data analysis is, after all, a tool for investigating phenomena of all kinds. The same approaches that students use in this unit can be called on for an investigation in science or social studies. Making these connections explicit and helping students transfer what they have learned here to new areas will give them an appreciation of the usefulness of mathematics throughout the curriculum. ■

SORTING: GROUPS AND GRAPHS
UNIT OVERVIEW

Sorting: Groups and Graphs is a unit of study that introduces sorting and classification as a way of organizing data. Suitable for students in grades 2 and 3, it provides a foundation for further work in statistics and data analysis, including the three upper-grade units in the *Used Numbers* series. In *Sorting: Groups and Graphs*, students:

▼ investigate similarities and differences in sets of related objects, people, or data

▼ classify these groups according to particular attributes and sort the members of the group accordingly

▼ collect real data through observation, experiments, and surveys

▼ construct their own categories for sorting these data

▼ represent these data in a variety of ways

▼ use their categories to describe and compare data sets

▼ formulate hypotheses and build theories about the reality represented by the data

How to use this unit

Like all the *Used Numbers* units, *Sorting: Groups and Graphs* is organized into investigations that may extend from one to five class sessions. To cover the entire unit requires approximately 18 class sessions of about 45 minutes each. Additional optional sessions and extensions are provided as well. Teachers who have used this unit have found that a schedule of 2–3 sessions per week works best to maintain continuity while allowing enough time for reflection and consolidation between sessions. The activities are sequenced so that students move gradually from more straightforward to more

complex investigations. The investigations are grouped into three parts:

▼ **Part 1: Introduction to sorting**
Sorting people: Who fits my rule?
Yekttis: What has a square head, one antenna, and doughnut eyes?

▼ **Part 2: Sorting and classifying data**
"Thing collections": What goes with what?

▼ **Part 3: Projects in data analysis**
Animals in the neighborhood
Investigating scary things

The three parts work well as a single five- to six-week unit. Some teachers have substituted this unit for their textbook chapters on graphs or data. Others have used it late in the year as a way to consolidate students' mathematical learning, knowing that it brings together work in counting, sorting, estimation, computation, graphing, and data collection in a problem-solving context. The parts can also be spaced over the entire school year. For example, some teachers use Part 1 in September to start off their work in mathematics. They return to Part 2 in January and use Part 3 in May when students have been together for most of the school year and are more able to work independently. Within each part, it is important that 2–3 sessions take place each week so that the experiences build on each other, allowing students gradually to acquire skills and understanding in data analysis.

Planning the investigations

In this book, you will find four types of information for each investigation:

Investigation overview. This section includes (1) a summary of the student activity, (2) materials you will need for the investigation and any special arrangements you may need to make, and (3) a list of the important mathematical ideas you will be emphasizing. Plan to look carefully at this overview a day or two before launching the investigation.

Session activities. For each session, you will find step-by-step suggestions that outline the students' explorations and the teacher's role. Although suggestions for questions and instructions are given, you will of course modify what you say to reflect your own style and the needs of your students. In all cases, the teacher's words are intended to be guidelines, *not* word-for-word scripts. Plan to read through this section

before each session to get the general flow of the activities in your mind.

Dialogue Boxes. The Dialogue Boxes illustrate the special role of discussion in these investigations and convey the nature of typical student-teacher interactions. Examples are drawn from the actual experiences of classes that have used these investigations. They call attention to issues that are likely to arise, typical student confusions and difficulties, and ways in which you can guide and support students in their mathematical thinking. Plan to read the relevant Dialogue Boxes before each session to help prepare for interactions with your students.

Teacher Notes. These sections provide important information you will need in presenting this unit. Here you will find explanations of key aspects of collecting, sorting, and analyzing data, including ways to graph data and how and when to introduce basic mathematical ideas. The Teacher Notes are listed in the contents because many are useful as references throughout the unit, not just where they first appear. You might plan to read them all for background information before starting the unit, then review them as needed when they come up in particular investigations.

Goals for students

The "Important mathematical ideas" listed in the investigation overviews highlight the particular student goals for those sessions.

Once goals are introduced in one part of the unit, they continue to be developed through experiences later in the unit. The major goals introduced in each part of *Sorting: Groups and Graphs*, are as follows:

Part 1: Introduction to sorting

Examining carefully the differences and similarities in a group of related objects or related data. Observing or considering the things to be sorted provides an initial sense of what categories might prove interesting. As the unit progresses and students gain more experience, they will notice more subtle and varied attributes of the groups they examine.

Making decisions about how to categorize data. Most categorical data can be grouped or classified in many different ways. Making decisions about what categories are important is a key idea in analyzing categorical data. As students collect their own data, they make decisions about what categories to use and which data belong in which categories.

Using negative information to clarify the definition of a category. In order for a category to be meaningful, it must *include* some things and *exclude* others. Understanding what does not fit in a category is a key to understanding what does fit.

Making sketches of the data. Graphs, pictures, tables, sketches, and tallies are working tools that are used to organize data. Students should be developing a repertoire of simple ways to display data quickly and clearly. They may use ways modeled by the teacher and also invent their own representations. In this unit, they are introduced to a concrete representation (interconnecting cubes) for recording data as well as to simple tables, graphs, tallies, and Venn diagrams.

Part 2: Sorting and classifying data

Thinking flexibly about the characteristics of the data. Most collections of objects or data from the real world are complex sets with many characteristics. As students sort objects or data themselves or try to figure out how others have sorted them, they must think about the characteristics of these objects or data in many different ways, shifting their points of view in order to see relationships that may not be immediately obvious.

Articulating logical reasoning. As students gain further experience with developing and defining categories, they can begin to explain how they came to a decision, give reasons for their ideas, explicate their definitions, and substantiate their conjectures. Students grapple with the challenges of being precise, clear, and accurate in describing similarities and differences in categorical data.

Constructing categories to describe the data. Students construct their own categories to describe data they have collected.

Deciding on categories ahead of time may obscure what is really interesting about the data; only through looking carefully at the data and their characteristics and sorting them in different ways can students begin to discover what the data may reveal.

Inventing representations of data. Students are encouraged to use a wide variety of invented pictures, sketches, tables, and graphs to portray their findings. They have the opportunity to see each other represent the same data in different ways. In this way students gain new ideas about picturing data and begin to learn how different representations can communicate different information about the data.

Building theories about the data. Collecting, representing, and considering data lead to developing descriptions and theories about aspects of the real world. Even young children can *use* their data as a basis for conjecturing, describing, generalizing, and wondering.

Part 3: Projects in data analysis

Collecting and recording survey data. For the first time, students collect and record data from outside of the classroom. They will need to think about how to ask their questions and how to record people's answers accurately.

Comparing two data sets. Throughout this unit, students have been looking carefully at similarities and differences. In this part of the unit, this process is expanded as students compare one whole set of data to another set of data and try to interpret what they notice.

Experiencing all the phases of a data analysis investigation. Students have time to collect, think about, categorize, display, compare, and interpret data during a more sustained investigation. Parallel to the phases of the writing process, a data analysis investigation includes "brainstorming"— discussion of the problem and collection of preliminary data; "rough draft" representations to organize preliminary results; analyses leading to refinement of ideas; and final "publication" through reports of results. The final project in this unit gives students a chance to experience all phases of this process. ■

Sorting: Groups and Graphs

PART 1
Introduction to sorting

SORTING PEOPLE: WHO FITS MY RULE?

INVESTIGATION OVERVIEW

What happens

In this investigation, students observe, classify, count, and record data about themselves. In Sessions 1 and 2, they learn to play "Guess My Rule," a classification game in which students try to figure out, by careful observation and questioning, what a group of things has in common. They will encounter this game in different contexts throughout the unit. At first, *you* establish the secret categories; later, small groups of students choose the categories for the game. As part of this game, data are counted and recorded. In Session 3, students collect and represent data about themselves, using interconnecting cubes to show the results. These whole-class surveys prepare students for working in small groups in Session 4 to decide on a survey question, take a survey of their classmates, then organize and represent the data they collect.

The activities take four class sessions of about 30–45 minutes. Sessions 1 and 2 can be done as one long (60–80 minutes) or two shorter (30–40 minutes) sessions, depending on how long it takes for students to guess the small groups' rules.

What to plan ahead of time

▼ Make sure there is a space in the classroom where a group of students can stand and be visible to the rest of the class (Sessions 1 and 2).

▼ Save the data you record about the class in Sessions 1 and 2 for use in Session 3.

▼ Provide interconnecting cubes, such as Unifix cubes. For Session 3, you will need the same number of cubes as students in your class; for Session 4, you will need about 200 cubes for a class of 25.

▼ Provide copies of the class list for students to use in taking their surveys (Session 3).

▼ Provide materials for making sketches of the data, including plain paper, lined or squared paper, and markers or crayons (Session 4).

Important mathematical ideas

Thinking flexibly about the characteristics of the data. Given a set of related things, such as neighborhood animals, we might notice any of several characteristics of the individuals in the set. The attribute game "Guess My Rule" is used throughout the unit to help students observe different characteristics, sort collections in different ways, and describe similarities and differences.

Using negative information to clarify the definition of a category. In order for a category to be meaningful, it must *include* some things and *exclude* others. Understanding what does *not* fit in a category is a key to understanding what does fit.

Making decisions about how to categorize data. Most categorical data can be grouped or classified in many different ways. Making decisions about what categories are important is part of analyzing categorical data. As students collect their own data, they make decisions about what categories to use as well as which data belong in which categories.

Making sketches of the data. Graphs, pictures, tables, sketches, and tallies are working tools that we can use to organize data. Students should be developing a repertoire of simple ways to display data quickly and clearly, as discussed in the Teacher Note, *Sketching data.* They may use methods modeled by the teacher and also invent their own representations. In this investigation, they use a concrete representation (interconnecting cubes) for recording data as well as simple sketches, graphs, and tallies.

Using more than one representation to view data. Different types of graphs or pictures can reveal different aspects of the same data. While working in small groups, students have the opportunity to see the same data graphed in different ways, by different people, giving them the chance to compare different views of the data. ∎

SESSION 1 AND 2 ACTIVITIES

Introducing the unit

Using your own words, tell the students briefly that, as part of their mathematics work, they will be doing research about collections of things and trying to figure out which things "go together." They will be thinking about themselves, about a strange group of alien creatures, about collections of miscellaneous small objects, about neighborhood animals, and about scary things. Sometimes they will be making graphs or lists or charts to show what they have decided about which things can be grouped together.

When scientists and mathematicians study the world, they often try to understand how things are the same and different. Sometimes things "go together" one way, but if you start thinking about them differently, they can "go together" in an entirely new way. For example, some people might say that all second graders "go together" because they are all in the second grade; but some people might say that *certain* second graders "go with" certain first and third and fourth graders because they all play baseball, or they all like the same kind of books, or they all walk to school.

If you can, use some specific examples from your own classroom or school of how students "go together" in different ways, depending on what characteristics you pay attention to.

For more information about classification and student thinking, see the Teacher Note, *Classification: A critical process in mathematics and science* (page 17).

Playing "Guess My Rule"

Because there are so many different ways things can go together, you are going to have to be very careful observers and pay attention to a lot of different characteristics of things. You'll be trying to figure out how things go together when we play a game called "Guess My Rule." Today we're going to play the game using people in this class.

Unless your students have a lot of experience with classification activities, it's a good idea to start with a straightforward, visually obvious rule, such as BROWN HAIR, WEARING RED, or WEARING A SWEATER. Choose two students who fit your rule and have them stand up in a designated area where other students can see them. For more information, see the Teacher Note, *Playing "Guess My Rule"* (page 18).

I have a Mystery Rule in mind that tells something about people in this class. It's something you can see. Some people fit my rule and some people don't. Katie and Sam both fit my rule. Katie and Sam, please go stand by the chalkboard where everyone can see you. Who thinks they know someone else who should stand with Katie and Sam? Don't tell me what you think my rule is! Right now, I just want you to tell me who else you think might go in the

group with Katie and Sam.

Students take turns saying who they think might fit the rule. If the person does fit, ask him or her to stand with those who fit the rule. If the person named does *not* fit the rule, send him or her to stand in another area designated for those who don't fit. (Alternatively, those who don't fit can stand at their seats.)

Stress the importance of all the clues—both those who fit the rule and those who don't. Prolong the clue-gathering until many students have had a chance to contribute guesses about which students do (or don't) fit. See the Dialogue Box, *"Guess My Rule" with people,* page 16, for an example of how clues are gathered as the game progresses.

When enough evidence has been gathered and you sense that most students have a good idea about the rule, allow students to say what they think the rule is. Ask them about the reasons for their conjectures. Of course, it's possible that students will come up with categories that *do* fit the evidence, but are not what you had in mind. If this happens, acknowledge the student's good reasoning, even though it did not lead to your secret rule.

Continue the game with one or two more secret rules of your choosing until everyone has a good feel for the game. Students are often very eager to contribute, and their enthusiasm may lead to lots of noise and movement. As long as the focus remains on the game, a little extra noise can be part of a productive activity.

Collecting and recording data: Small groups choose a rule

Divide the class into groups of three. Each group decides on and writes down a Mystery Rule describing some students in the class. Have each group show you their rule secretly and make sure their category is one that can be readily seen and understood by the other students. (See the Teacher Note, *Playing "Guess My Rule,"* page 18, for guidelines to help students choose their rules.)

Reconvene the entire class and let each group challenge the others to "guess my rule." Use the conventions you established earlier about where to stand if you *do* or *don't* fit the rule. Support each group in giving consistent feedback as the other students choose individuals who might fit the rule. As before, delay conjectures about what the rule is until many students have had a chance to suggest who they think fits.

After each rule is guessed, record the number of students who do and do not fit the rule on the chalkboard or large paper. For example:

Wearing a watch: 9
Not wearing a watch: 14

Buttons   ✓✓✓✓✓✓✓✓✓
No buttons   ✓✓✓✓✓✓✓✓✓✓

Record the data *in a different way* for each rule, in order to model a variety of ways of keeping track of data. You can use pictures, numbers, tallies, checkmarks, and so forth. See the Teacher Note, *Sketching data* (page 24), for further suggestions. Also ask the students for their ideas about how to record the data.

Who can think of a way we can show how many students have brown hair—one that's different from the ways we have used so far?

Encourage variety and innovation.

It is hard to predict how long it will take for the class to guess each rule. Typically, some rules are guessed quickly (within 2–3 minutes) while others take longer.

Save the data from the small-group rules for the next session.

Extensions

Students usually enjoy this activity so much that you can continue to play it throughout the unit. One or two rounds of "Guess My Rule" with people will fit in nicely at odd times—before lunch, at the end of the day, or whenever you have a free 10 minutes.

Use the data collected from the small-group rules for investigating addition and subtraction strategies. For example, pose questions such as this:

If there are 23 students here today, and 9

are wearing watches, how could we find out how many students are *not* wearing watches without counting them? Such discussions can emphasize thinking of many different strategies for solving the problem, not just coming up with the right answer. ■

𝟞𝟞𝟡𝟡DIALOGUE BOX
"Guess My Rule" with people

In the following dialogue, the teacher's Mystery Rule is WEARING GREEN.

Katie and Sam both fit the rule I'm thinking of. Let's have people who fit my rule stand up here. [*Katie and Sam stand up in front of the chalkboard.*] **Who thinks they know someone else who might fit in this group? Don't tell me the rule, if you think you know it; just tell me another person you think might fit.**

JANE: Do I fit?

Yes, you do fit my rule. [*Jane joins Katie and Sam. It happens that all three children selected so far have blond hair. This characteristic is visually striking when they all stand together.*]

SERENA [*who also has blond hair*]: I think I fit.

No, you don't fit the Mystery Rule, but I bet I know what you might have been thinking about. Stand over by my desk to start the "people who don't fit the rule" group. Serena is an important clue.

EDDIE: I know what the rule is! It's . . .

Don't tell the rule yet. If you think you know, tell me someone else who fits.

EDDIE: Um . . . [*Looks around, can't find anyone.*]

What about yourself?

EDDIE: I don't think I fit.

OK. Go stand with Serena so people have more clues for who *doesn't* fit.

[*Later*] . . .

LENA: Does Christina fit? [*Christina is wearing a green shirt and pants.*]

Yes, she does fit—that's another important clue.-

GLENN: I know! I know!

OTHERS: Me, too! I know the rule!

OK, let's see if anyone else fits the rule. Then you can say what you think it is.

☞ In this conversation, the teacher keeps the focus on looking carefully at all the evidence, rather than on getting the right answer quickly. She uses Serena's sensible guess to point out the value of negative information: Even though Serena does not fit the rule, she provides an important clue in narrowing down the possibilities. By prolonging the discussion and gathering more clues, the teacher gives more students the time to think and come to their own conclusions. ■

✎ TEACHER NOTE
Classification: A critical process in mathematics and science

This unit, *Sorting: Groups and Graphs*, focuses on collecting, organizing, and interpreting data that can be placed in categories. In the primary grades, much of the data that interests children is *categorical* data, data that is based on counting the members of certain related categories. For example, students might do a survey of the modes of transportation they use to get to school (how many walk, how many take the bus, how many ride a bicycle), or undertake a study of the weather throughout the year (how many days are cloudy, how many are sunny, how many are rainy, and so forth). Students sort the data they collect into categories and make comparisons by counting.

This unit of study blends work in classification and work in data analysis. Classification is a critical tool in collecting, organizing, and interpreting data. Classifying data involves complex thinking. This unit develops two particularly important thinking habits.

First, *classification involves students in thinking flexibly about the characteristics of the data.* Given a set of related things, such as neighborhood animals, we could focus on many different characteristics. Classification of animals is a real-world problem for scientists: What makes a bird a bird? Is a whale more closely related to a cow than to a trout? Which characteristics will reveal whether a raccoon is related to an opossum? Recent studies showing that some birds may be descended from dinosaurs show how startling the results of careful classification can be. In order to do classification, students need to be flexible, paying attention to all the attributes of the thing they are studying. Students in the second and third grades are beginning to develop this flexibility, as their focus widens from single attributes to the relationships among more than one attribute. The attribute game "Guess My Rule" encourages this flexibility by leading students to observe different characteristics, sort collections in different ways, and describe similarities and differences in a group of things.

Second, *classification involves students in making decisions about how to categorize data in different ways* in order to help them interpret what the data show about the world. Most categorical data can be grouped or classified in many different ways. Consider the following example:

Suppose that, as principal of the elementary school, you were interested in safety issues related to how students get to school in the morning. You might collect data on their modes of transportation and sort it like this:

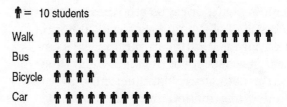

This classification shows the mode of transportation used by each student. However, after looking at the data this way, you might decide that what you really need to know is how many students have to cross the dangerous intersection in front of the school. You could then resort the data this way:

Then you might realize that the students who bicycle also have to cross the intersection by themselves. So you reclassify the data again, like this:

Each of these classifications gives different information about the transportation used by students. Depending on how you classify, you can get some information from the graph, but other information is hidden.

As students work with data they have collected, they will make their own decisions about what categories to use and which data belong in which categories. Defining and redefining categories, as students will do in the last half of the unit, is a critical part of data analysis. Sorting in various ways can reveal new aspects of the data. Each time we view the data somewhat differently, we can gain new information about the world. ■

✎ TEACHER NOTE
Playing "Guess My Rule"

"Guess My Rule" is a classification guessing game in which players try to figure out the common characteristic, or attribute, of a set of objects. If you have attribute blocks or logic blocks in your classroom, you may be familiar with this game. (For information about commercially available attribute materials, see the Teacher Note, *Using the Yektti set*, page 29.)

"Guess My Rule" is played throughout this unit in different contexts, but the students first play it in a context very familiar to them: themselves. To play the game, the rule-maker (who may be you, a student, or a group of students) decides on a secret Mystery Rule for classifying a particular group of things. For example, classification rules for people might be everyone who is WEARING ORANGE, or everyone who has BROWN HAIR.

The rule-maker starts the game by giving some examples of people who fit the rule—for example, by having two students who are wearing orange stand up. The guessers then try to find other individuals who might fit the rule: "Can Sandy fit your rule?"

With each guess, the individual named is added either to the group that *does* fit or to the group that *does not* fit the rule. Both groups must be clearly visible to the guessers

so they can make use of all the evidence—both what does and does not fit—as they try to figure out what the rule might be.

Two guidelines are particularly important to stress during play:

"Wrong" guesses are clues that are just as important as "right" guesses. "No, Glenn doesn't fit, but that's important evidence. Think about how Glenn is different from Elisabeth, Maya, and Eddie." Here is a wonderful opportunity to help students learn that errors are not just mistakes but can be important sources of information.

When you think you know what the rule is, test your theory by giving another example, not by revealing the rule. "Jane, you look like you're sure you know what the rule is. We don't want to give it away yet, so let's test out your theory. Tell me someone who you think does fit the rule." Requiring students to add new evidence, rather than making a guess, serves two purposes. It allows students to test their theories without revealing their guess to other students. And, it provides more information and more time to think for students who do not yet have a theory of their own.

When students begin choosing rules themselves, they sometimes think of rules that are either too vague (students WEARING DIFFERENT COLORS) or too difficult for other students to guess (students WITH A PIECE OF THREAD HANGING FROM THEIR SHIRTS). You can guide and support students in choosing rules that are "medium hard"—not so obvious that everyone will see them immediately, but not so hard that no one will be able to figure them out. The students should be clear about who would fit their rule *and* who would not fit; this eliminates rules like WEARING DIFFERENT COLORS which everyone will probably fit. It's also important to pick a rule about something people can see. That is, one rule for classifying might be LIKES BASEBALL, but no one will be able to figure out this rule by just looking.

"Guess My Rule" can be very dramatic. Keep the mystery and drama high with remarks such as, "That was an important clue," "This is very tricky," "I think maybe Sam has a good idea now," and "I bet I know what Marjorie's theory is."

It is surprising how hard it can be to guess what seems to be a very obvious rule (like WEARING GREEN). Teachers have found that it is often difficult to predict in advance which rules will be more difficult than others. Sometimes one that you think will be tough is guessed right away; at other times, a rule that seemed "obvious" will turn out to be impossible! Sometimes it will be necessary to give additional clues when students are stuck. For example, one teacher chose HAS BUTTONS as her Mystery Rule. After all the students had been placed in one of the two groups, still no one could guess the rule. So she moved down the line of children, drawing attention to each in turn: "Look carefully at David's front. . . . Now I'm going to turn

Maureen around to the back, like this—see what you can see. . . . You have to look really hard at Caroline—look along her arms." Finally, students guessed the rule.

Since classification is a process used in many disciplines, you can easily adapt the game to other subject areas. A language arts version of "Guess My Rule" with words is suggested as an extension in the Yektti investigation (page 34). Teachers have also used "Guess My Rule" in social studies and science as well as other aspects of mathematics. Animals, states, historical figures, geometric shapes, types of food, and countless other items can all be classified in different ways.

Being able to see how things go together improves, like many things, with experience. As you and your students play this game repeatedly in different contexts, you will find yourselves becoming more observant and more flexible in your thinking about similarities and differences. ■

HAS BUTTONS

Collecting and recording data: Using interconnecting cubes

Make sure students can see the data you collected in the previous sessions. Remind students that you looked at how students in the class are the same and different, how they can be grouped in different ways.

Last time you thought about [who has BROWN HAIR, who was WEARING STRIPES, who HAD BUTTONS, who HAD ANYTHING IN THEIR HAIR, and . . .]. Here is the information we collected about each group. Who remembers what we found out about BROWN HAIR? . . . Who can tell me what this sketch about BUTTONS shows? . . . Do you think, if we made the same groups today, that any of these numbers would be different? Would some be the same?

Let students freely express their views. Follow up with questions that probe their reasoning.

Does anyone agree or disagree with Carlos that [BROWN HAIR] wouldn't change? Is there anything that you are *sure* will be different? Why do you think that?

Choose one of the categories about which there has been some discussion.

Let's try [BROWN HAIR] again. Some of you think the results will be exactly the same.

We're going to use these cubes to see if that's true. Later you'll be using these cubes in your small groups to record information, so I want you to see how to use them. Everyone who [has BROWN HAIR] come up and take one of these cubes. Then we'll put them together to see how many people [have BROWN HAIR].

Choose one color of cubes to make the tower. Each student who fits the category attaches a cube of that color to make a tower of cubes.

Describing the data: Are the results what we expected?

Hold up the tower and, with the students, count the cubes. Allow time for students to discuss the results. Are the results what they expected? Why or why not? See the Dialogue Box, *Discussing class data* (page 21).

Ask students how they would make a tower to show students who do *not* fit the category [e.g., students who do not have BROWN HAIR]. This is a good opportunity for students to discuss addition and subtraction strategies, as demonstrated in the Dialogue Box, *Discussing class data* (page 21). Make the second tower. This time, have each student in the "doesn't fit" group come up and attach a cube to the tower, as the first group did.

Repeat the activity with one or two of the other categories from the previous sessions.

Considering the problem: Planning a class survey

Students now work in small groups to decide on a survey question, take a survey of their classmates, then organize and represent their data. At this age level, pairs or threes work best to ensure participation of all students. For students who are experienced in small-group work, groups of four are sometimes successful.

Before students break up into their small groups, explain that they will be doing a survey of their classmates. This survey will focus on something that can be seen about everybody in the class. Remind them of some of the characteristics they explored in the previous session (e.g., color of clothes worn, eye color, type of shoes worn, hairstyle). In their small groups, their task will be to

▼ decide on what characteristic they will investigate;

▼ collect data, using a class list, about everyone in the class; and

▼ show what they found out in several different ways.

Each group decides on their characteristic, writes it down, and shows it to you. If necessary, help students clarify the characteristic they are investigating. Some students may stick to a characteristic that can be divided into two groups (e.g., students WITH

WATCHES, students WITHOUT WATCHES), while others may decide they want to investigate a characteristic that has several categories, such as eye color (e.g., BROWN, BLUE, GREEN, HAZEL).

Collecting and recording the data: Taking the survey

Hand out a copy of the class list to each group. Give help where needed, but encourage groups to organize themselves and to make their own decisions throughout this activity. Who will do what in their group? How will they be sure they have collected data from every student? How will they make sure their data are accurate?

Since the data-collecting part of this activity involves a lot of moving around, you may want to invoke the following rule (which is also fun): *Students may talk only to those in their own small group.* In order to collect their data, they must walk around and gather information by observation. If absolutely necessary, they can use sign language to "talk" to someone else (e.g., pointing to get someone to look up so you can see their eye color).

It is appropriate to introduce the word *data* as it arises naturally in this session or the next one. See the Teacher Note, *What are data, anyway?* (page 22). ■

66 99 DIALOGUE BOX
Discussing class data

In this class of 23, the 15 students with brown hair have each taken a brown Unifix cube out of the box and put them into a tower of 15 cubes. The students counted the number of cubes as the teacher pointed to each cube in the tower.

So we have 15 people with BROWN HAIR? Is that what you expected?

[*Yes and no are heard from various students.*]

But why? Let's hear from the people who said yes and the people who said no.

ELISABETH: Well, it was 15 yesterday, and people don't have different hair color every day!

So, you thought . . . ?

ELISABETH: It would still be 15, and it was.

SEAN: I don't get it.

What don't you get, Sean?

SEAN: Well, I thought it would come out the same, too, but then when you were saying about yesterday, remember Billy said he wasn't here, and Billy has BROWN HAIR.

What do other people think about what Sean is saying?

JESSICA: We didn't count Billy yesterday, so today it should be 16.

TONY: We counted wrong.

We counted wrong?

TONY: Yeah, we could have counted wrong today or yesterday.

Maybe, although the counters were pretty careful yesterday, and they checked each other. Is there any other explanation?

LYNNE: Maybe we didn't count all the same people.

Maybe we didn't count all the same people. That's an interesting idea. Is it possible we didn't count the same people?

ROSA: Well, when we were deciding who to count, we couldn't decide if Maya had BROWN HAIR or BLACK HAIR.

ALAN: And Mark said my hair was BROWN, but it's BLOND.

So is Lynne right? Did we count differently yesterday?

ALAN: No, because I didn't get counted yesterday and neither did Maya, and we didn't count today either.

Well, this is a mystery then . . .

KATIE: But Dennis isn't here today.

So what would that . . .

AMY: I get it, it's like switched. Yesterday we counted Dennis and today we counted Billy.

I'm not sure I quite get it. Who can explain what Amy is saying?

KATIE: Yeah, it works. Yesterday Dennis was here and he has BROWN HAIR and we got 15.

So then today Dennis isn't here, so it would be 14, but then we added Billy, so it's 15 again.

GLENN: It's 15 both days, but it's not the same kids.

KIMARA: We really have 16 altogether if you take the 15 today and you add Dennis.

OK, I'm going to add a cube to the tower for Dennis. Now there are 16 cubes in the BROWN HAIR tower. How many cubes do we need for a DON'T HAVE BROWN HAIR tower?

VARIOUS STUDENTS: Six . . . no, 7.

Is it 6 or 7? Who has a good strategy for showing how many of you are in the NOT BROWN HAIR group?

PAUL [*counting on his fingers*]: 17, 18, 19, 20, 21, 22, 23, that's 7 more.

OK, that works. Could I do that with the cubes?

PAUL: Yeah, put a cube on for every kid up to 23.

[*The teacher asks each student who doesn't have brown hair to come up and add an orange cube to the tower. As they do so, the class counts together: 17, 18, 19, 20, 21, 22, 23. Then she separates the 7 orange cubes from the rest of the tower, and they count them in unison.*]

So, we can tell by Paul's method that we have 7 people in the NOT BROWN HAIR group. Who has a different way we can tell that 7 people don't have BROWN HAIR?

(Dialogue Box continued)

JESSICA: We could count the people!

OK, we could. Should we do that? [*Many students say yes.*] **Everyone who doesn't have BROWN HAIR, stand up, and let's count.** [*They count, and there are 7 students standing.*] **We counted cubes and we counted people. Suppose we didn't count. We know there are 16 brown-haired people in this tower. Any other way we could know there are 7 people who belong in the other tower?**

TONY: Well, there's 23 in the class, so it's 16, so 4 more would be to 20, and then 3 more to 23, that's 7.

Nice strategy. Who has a different one? Kimara?

KIMARA: OK. You know that 16 and 6 would be 22, cause that's like 6 and 6 is 12, so it has to be one more, so it's 7.

JANE: I have one. You can do it by twos—18, 20, 22, so that's 2, 2, 2 is 6, but then you have to do 1 more to get to 23.

☞ In this class, the teacher knows that some of the students still need to see the concrete one-to-one connection between a student and a cube, while others are able to think about the relationship between the two groups in their heads. Many students at this age level need both; they are most comfortable and convinced when they can actually count the students who don't have brown hair, but they are also beginning to play with number strategies. In order to cope with this diversity, the teacher follows the suggestion

that they count the actual students but also encourages students to think of strategies for manipulating the numbers themselves. This teacher rarely asks for an answer in arithmetic without asking for as many strategies as the students can think of for "proving" their answer, so the students are beginning to develop a repertoire of such strategies. At another time, she might spend more time drawing pictures illustrating students' strategies or having students explain their strategies to each other. ■

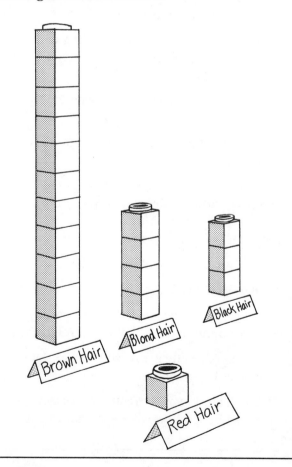

I'm 48 inches tall.

This bottle holds 2 liters of soda pop.

She is wearing sneakers.

These shoes weigh 150 grams.

Each of these statements contains descriptive information or *data* about some person or thing. Data is a plural noun; one *datum* is a single fact. Data are the facts, or the information, that differentiate and describe people, objects, or other entities (e.g., countries). Data may be expressed as numbers (e.g., he is 48 inches tall; she has 4 people in her family) or attributes (her favorite flavor is chocolate; his hair is curly).

Data are collected through surveys, observation, measuring, counting, and experiments. If we study rainfall, we might collect rain and measure the amount that falls each day. If we study hair color, we might observe and record the color of each person's hair.

Collecting data involves detailed judgments about how to count, measure, or describe. Should we record rainfall data for each day or for each rainstorm? Should we round off to the nearest inch? Should we count just one color for a person's hair? Should we record "yellow" or "dirty blond" or "gold"? Should "brown" be a single category, or should it be divided into several shades?

Once data are collected, recorded, counted, and analyzed, we can use them as the basis for making decisions. In one school, for example, a study of accidents on a particular piece of playground equipment showed that most of the accidents involved children who were in first, second, or third grade. Those who studied the data realized that the younger students' hands were too small to grasp the bars firmly enough. A decision to keep primary grade children off this equipment was made because the *data*, or the *facts*, led to that conclusion.

When students collect data, they are collecting facts. When they interpret these data, they are developing theories or generalizations. The data provide the basis for their theories. ■

SESSION 4 ACTIVITIES

Organizing the data: Pictures, sketches, and graphs

Tell students that they are now going to be showing in several different ways what they found out in their surveys. Students work in their small groups. First, they show their data with interconnecting cubes. Remind students about the way they used cubes earlier to show the results from "Guess My Rule." For some students, this concrete representation is an important connection between the real people and a representation on paper.

Then ask *each* student to make a picture or a sketch on paper, showing the data they collected, as a group. This picture is a way to show someone else what they found out. The emphasis of this session is on having

students invent their own ways of representing their data. See the Teacher Note, *Sketching data* (page 24), for examples. Encourage the students in a single group to each use a *different* way to show their data. Students in the same group will benefit from seeing their teammates showing exactly the same data in different ways.

Extensions

Some teachers link classification activities with multicultural studies. A look at family origins, language, and culture in order to help students understand and appreciate cultural diversity can be a rewarding and rich experience in a classroom. During such a study, students can sort photographs or name cards of everyone in the class and/or undertake surveys that focus on such characteristics as where students were born, what languages they speak, or where their ancestors are from. ■

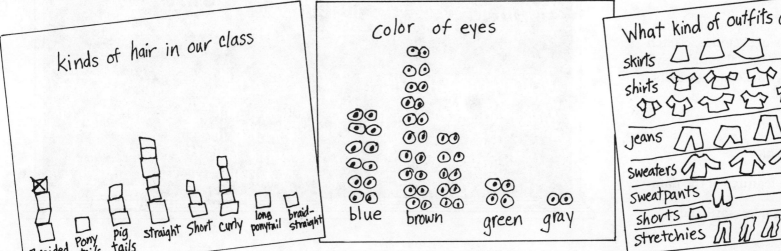

✎ TEACHER NOTE
Sketching data

Graphs are traditionally the focus for instruction in statistics in the elementary grades, even though the process of doing statistics involves much more than simply making and reading graphs. Most of us think of graphs as the endpoint of the data analysis process. Mathematicians and scientists, however, use pictures and graphs during the process of analysis as tools for understanding the data. Representing data is an attempt to organize the data so that we can see overall characteristics more clearly.

Our students must gain facility with creating pictures, diagrams, tallies, tables, graphs, or concrete models that provide a first quick look at the data. We call these representations "sketches" in order to emphasize that they are working representations, rather than final products.

We want students to become comfortable with a variety of types of sketches. Sketch graphs should be easy to make and easy to read; they should not challenge students' patience or fine motor skills.

Sketch graphs:

▼ can be made rapidly

▼ reveal important features of the data

▼ are clear, but not necessarily neat

▼ don't require labels or titles (as long as students are clear about what they are looking at)

▼ don't require time-consuming attention to color or design

▼ may not be precise, straight, or perfectly aligned

Sketch graphs might be made with pencil and paper, with Unifix cubes, or with stick-on notes (such as Post-it notes). Cubes and stick-on notes offer flexibility since they can easily be rearranged. Encourage students in the second and third grades to construct concrete and pictorial representations of their data, using interlocking cubes, their own pictures, or even the actual objects. Also model for students a variety of quick sketches, including forms of simple bar graphs and tallies.

Encourage students to invent and use different forms until they discover some that work well in organizing their data. Students in the second and third grade are capable of inventing simple, but effective, sketches and pictures of the data they collect, like the examples shown in this Teacher Note.

At this age level, stress making clear and organized representations, but do not require precision. Students may not make uniform squares for their bar graph or line up their pictorial symbols evenly (see page 23), but if their sketch helps them describe and interpret their data, they are well on their way to developing important skills in data analysis. ■

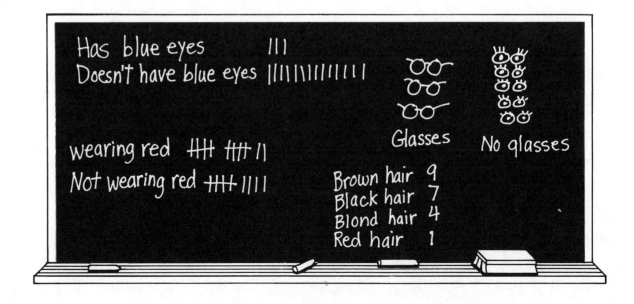

YEKTTIS:
WHAT HAS A SQUARE HEAD, ONE ANTENNA, AND DOUGHNUT EYES?

INVESTIGATION OVERVIEW

What happens

This investigation takes a trip into fantasy with a look at the Yekttis (YEK-tees). Like scientists studying a newly discovered form of life, students discover the attributes of the Yekttis through an activity led by the teacher. They then play "Guess My Rule" with a set of cards portraying all the individual Yekttis. The "Guess My Rule" game becomes more complex as students learn to consider more than one rule at a time. Venn diagrams are introduced as a way to represent the different Yekti attributes.

The activities take four class sessions of about 30–45 minutes.

What to plan ahead of time

▼ Read about the Yekttis in the Teacher Note, *Using the Yekti set*, page 29 (Session 1).

▼ Pull out the full page Yekti pictures at the end of this book to make a set of large Yekti cards (Session 1).

▼ Prepare sets of small Yekti picture cards and word cards for each small group according to the guidelines in the Teacher Note, *Using the Yekti set*, page 29 (Sessions 2 and 4).

▼ Become familiar with using Venn diagrams to show two overlapping sets. See the Teacher Note, *Venn diagrams: Sorting by two attributes*, page 37 (Session 4).

▼ On a large piece of easel or chart paper, draw two non-overlapping circles (diagram A). On another piece, draw two overlapping circles (diagram B). Use a diameter of about 20 inches, with an overlap of about 10 inches.
You might use two loops of string or ribbon or hula hoops instead. You will need only one copy of the non-overlapping circles, but each small group will need its own copy of the overlapping circles (Session 4).

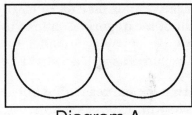
Diagram A

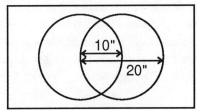
Diagram B

Important mathematical ideas

Examining carefully the differences and similarities in a group of related objects or related data. Observing or considering the things to be sorted provides an initial sense of what categories might prove interesting. Here, students have to decide which characteristics of a group of fantasy creatures matter—which are always the same, which vary. Later, when they work with sets of real data, they will have to make many similar decisions about how to classify their data. Deciding on categories ahead of time may obscure what is really interesting about the data; only through looking carefully at the data and their characteristics and sorting them in different ways can we begin to discover what the data may reveal.

Using negative information to clarify the definition of a category. Continue to stress the importance of paying attention to what a category excludes as well as what it includes.

Articulating logical reasoning. After several experiences with "Guess My Rule," students can begin to explain their thinking about how they used the evidence to figure out a category. Students at this age level will vary a great deal in how clearly and precisely they can verbalize their reasoning, but all can be encouraged to talk about their strategies, as shown in the Dialogue Box, *How did you know?*

Using Venn diagrams to show various relationships within a group of related objects. A Venn diagram—or, as your second and third graders may want to call it, a "circle diagram,"—is a special kind of representation that helps us show the results of sorting, as discussed in the Teacher Note, *Venn diagrams: Sorting by two attributes.* ∎

SESSION 1 ACTIVITIES

Introducing the Yekttis: A strange discovery

Read the following story to start off the investigation.

Lee and Anita, a pair of 8-year-old twins, discovered some strange creatures near their home in Wyoming. These creatures were living in abandoned prairie dog burrows next to a dirt road that the twins used as a shortcut on their way to school. Lee and Anita started studying these creatures. They visited them every chance they had. Because these creatures never came all the way out of their holes in the ground, Lee and Anita could see only their heads. The creatures looked as though they might have come from another planet.

Lee loved to make up codes and learn about languages. After a few months, he learned how to say some words in the creatures' own language, and he taught them a few words in English and in Spanish. He learned that the creatures called themselves Yekttis (YEK-tees), that they came from a very distant planet, and that they were peaceful creatures.

Anita liked to study different kinds of living things. She decided to do a report about the Yekttis for a science project at school. She made a sketch of the head of each of the Yekttis she had seen. She noticed that a lot of them were similar to each other, but that no two were exactly alike. She used her sketches to figure out how she could describe to other human beings what the Yekttis looked like.

Today we will look at copies of Anita's sketches and see if you can figure out how to describe the Yekttis.

Describing the Yekttis

Using the set of large Yektti cards, show the class a picture of just one Yektti.

I'm going to show you some Yekttis, one at a time. Here's the first one. What can you tell me about what a Yektti looks like? . . . Here's another Yektti. What do you see that's the same or that's different from the first one? Remember, Lee and Anita found out that the Yekttis were similar, but no two were exactly alike.

Gradually reveal more Yektti cards as students develop their descriptions. Challenge students to try to figure out the special characteristics of these creatures.

Now that you've seen quite a few of the Yekttis and you've made some observations about how they look, see if you can ask me for a particular Yektti that you think I might have here. Lynne said that this one has a square head and three antennas. Can anyone think of another one I might have that's like this one, but not exactly like it?

To stress the informational nature of each student's contributions, rather than whether or not a particular description is "correct,"

respond to each description with another piece of information. For example, suppose a student asks, "Do you have a Yektti with a square head and 5 antennas?" You might answer, "No, I don't have one with 5 antennas, but I have this square one with 4 antennas." (For further ideas, see the Dialogue Box, *Describing the set of Yekttis*, page 28.)

At the beginning of this activity, some students may have difficulty thinking about many characteristics at once. Choose Yekttis with the same head shape at first, until students have begun to realize that there are different eye types and different numbers of antennas. Then you can introduce new head shapes dramatically, just as students are feeling comfortable with the information they have deduced so far.

Keep the Yekttis they have identified visible, perhaps along the chalkboard ledge or held up by students standing in front of the group, while the class tries to figure out which ones they haven't yet identified.

Through questioning, students gradually infer the attributes of the Yekttis: the four head shapes, the four numbers of antenna, and the two eye types. After a while, you can ask students to specify completely all three attributes of the Yektti they want to see, e.g., "I want a triangle Yektti with one antenna and ringed eyes." (See the Dialogue Box, *Describing the set of Yekttis*, page 28.)

Students often come up with their own

descriptive vocabulary, especially to describe the Yekttis' eyes. Some have called the plain eyes "cookie eyes" or "hamburger eyes" and the ringed eyes "doughnut eyes" or "bagel eyes." Using the students' invented words for these descriptions is fine. The eyes are called *plain* and *ringed* on the game cards used in Session 2; eventually you will need to establish this common vocabulary.

When the discussion has touched on all the possible Yektti types, ask students to summarize the characteristics of Yekttis. They can list characteristics that all Yekttis have (a small mouth, no nose, no ears) and characteristics that differ (the four head shapes, the two eye types, and the number of antennas ranging from 1 to 4). There is no necessity to generate all 32 of the individual Yekttis, but some classes do enjoy figuring out every last one.

Developing theories

In many classes, students have spontaneously begun to develop theories about the characteristics of the Yekttis. For example, some speculated that Yekttis with one eye type were females, and those with the other eye type were males. Others have thought these might be adults and children. Another group speculated that the number of antennas was an indication of age: the more antennas, the older the Yekttis. Another part of this session's discussion can focus on student's theories, which might be incorporated in writing about the Yekttis if you decide to do the extension suggested in Session 4.

Extension

An advanced question is: How many Yekttis are there altogether if there is one Yektti with every possible combination of characteristics and no duplicates? Second and third graders have been able to make pictures or diagrams to figure out the solution. ■

❝❞DIALOGUE BOX
Describing the set of Yekttis

Here is one of the Yekttis. Can you figure out how Yekttis look?

STUDENTS: It looks like a triangle . . . It has antennas . . . It has big eyes . . . It has doughnut eyes . . . It has rings around it . . . like a bagel . . . It has a small mouth.

These are good descriptions. Let me show you another one.

STUDENTS: The eyes look like cookies . . . The mouth looks like a worm . . . It has only 1 antenna.

What did the other one have?

LYNNE: Three.

I'll show you another one.

MAYA: It only has 2 antennas.

MARK: I see a pattern. The first one had three—3, 2, 1! The next one probably has 4.

I do have one with 4 antennas. Here it is. Can anyone describe another Yektti I might have here?

ELISABETH: Do you have one with doughnut eyes?

I do. Here it is. Who can ask for another one?

EDDIE: One with 4 antennas.

I do have some with four antennas, but can you tell me more about the one you want?

EDDIE: And cookie eyes.

I do have one like that, here it is. [*Shows one with a square head.*] **Who can describe another Yektti?**

DENNIS: A square one with 3 antennas?

Yes. Actually I have two different square ones with 3 antennas. Can you tell me anything else about the one you want?

DENNIS: It has doughnut eyes!

BILLY: A round one with 3 antennas?

Nope, I don't have any round ones, but I do have some other Yekttis with 3 antennas, like this one. [*Shows a hexagon head with plain eyes and 3 antennas.*] **This shape is called a hexagon. It has six sides. You're the first person to figure out something that's not true about Yekttis, Billy. Who thinks they can tell me about a different hexagon Yektti?**

ROSA: A hexagon with 1 antenna.

Can you give me a little more information?

ROSA: With cookie eyes.

[*Later*] . . .

SAM: A diamond Yektti with 1 antenna and plain eyes.

Yes, I have one like that. Let's see, here it is. That was a careful description. I knew exactly which one you meant. Who else can look carefully and tell me all the information I need for another one that's not out yet?

LENA: The same but with 3 horns.

The same?

LENA: Yeah, a diamond with cookie eyes like the other one, but with 3 horns . . . no, we have that one already . . . with 2 horns.

PAUL: And a 4 one, the same with 4 antennas.

LENA: It's like a family.

CARLOS: Can I ask a question? How come . . . they probably get older and older and grow more antennas, like 1 and then they get 2.

ALAN: Yeah, maybe it's the baby with just 1 antenna.

SERENA: Or maybe the babies are born bald, but they stay underground, so you never see them unless they're old enough to have 1 antenna. ■

✎ TEACHER NOTE
Using the Yektti set

About the Yekttis

Yekttis (YEK-tees) are fantasy creatures from outer space. They have from 1 to 4 antennas, two types of eyes (ringed or plain), and four head shapes (square, triangle, diamond, or hexagon). The Yektti cards are essentially an attribute set, that is, a set of things that can be sorted and classified according to the characteristics of this set. Like other attribute materials, this set is structured so that there is exactly one Yektti with each possible combination of characteristics; for example, there is one triangular Yektti with 3 antennas and ringed eyes, one triangular Yektti with 3 antennas and plain eyes, one square Yektti with 3 antennas and plain eyes, and so forth.

Unlike most sets of related things in the real world, the Yektti set has only three attributes (number of antennas, head shape, eye type). Students have already dealt with a more complex set—themselves—which has endless possibilities for classification, and later in this unit they will be developing their own categories for groups of things with much less well-defined characteristics. However, attribute materials like the Yekttis are useful exactly because they are more limited. Because the Yekttis can be sorted into only a few categories that can be easily deduced,

students can concentrate on making careful observations and reasoning from evidence. In this investigation, students engage in sorting activities that require them to take into account more than one attribute at a time. The Yekttis help students learn about more complex sorting in a context that is not too overwhelming.

The Yektti materials

A complete Yektti set contains 32 individual Yekttis, one with each possible combination of head shape, eye type, and number of antennas. For this investigation, you will need one large Yektti set for whole class use and a small Yektti set for each small group. A large set is obtained by carefully removing the last 32 pages of this book. Small sets of cards for student use are commercially available from Dale Seymour Publications. Or, you can construct the sets yourself by duplicating and cutting apart the small Yektti pictures on pages 83–89. Laminating and/or mounting the Yektti cards on cardboard will give you more durable sets that can be used again and again.

For whole class work (Session 1), you will need only the large Yektti set. Some teachers have made large Yektti transparencies for use with an overhead projector. For small-group work (Session 2), each student group will need its own small set of 32 Yektti cards, plus a set of 10 word cards, which can be duplicated from page 82.

Work with sorting materials such as attribute block sets (sometimes called A-blocks), logic blocks, or people pieces is an appropriate extension throughout this unit. The game "Guess My Rule," as well as many other activities in which students investigate classification, can be done with these materials. Attribute materials are sets of blocks or drawings on cards that vary in shape, color, size, or other characteristics. The Yekttis in this unit are one version of attribute material. Another is the set of 32 Attribute Blocks originally developed by the Elementary Science Study. Four colors, four shapes, and two sizes are represented in the set, and there is one block for each possible combination of characteristics (e.g., one big yellow triangle, one small blue square). These are available from most distributors of mathematical manipulatives. The ESS *Attribute Blocks Teacher's Guide* is available from Delta Education, Inc., P.O. Box M, Nashua, NH 03061-6012. ∎

SESSION 2 ACTIVITIES

Small-group work: "Guess My Rule" with the Yektti cards

Divide the class into groups of three. Give each group a set of the small Yektti picture cards and a pack of Yektti word cards. Each group will be playing "Guess My Rule" with the Yektti card sets.

Students in the group take turns choosing a Mystery Rule about the Yekttis (for example, Yekttis with PLAIN EYES or Yekttis with THREE ANTENNAS). A student can either decide on a rule and then find the word card to match it, or simply look through the cards and select one as the secret rule. In either case, the word card describing the Mystery Rule should be placed facedown on the table. The word cards help students choose one rule and stick to it. They are also useful reminders if a student forgets which rule was chosen, and serve to reassure the guessers that there is a clear rule.

Once the Mystery Rule is chosen, the student picks out a Yektti picture card or two to start the game, saying something like, "These Yekttis fit my rule." Other students now take turns asking if a particular Yektti fits. If it does, that card is placed in the center of the playing area. If it doesn't fit, the card is placed to one side, or wherever the players decide to put the Yekttis that don't fit the rule.

☞ Remember, the ones that *don't fit* provide important information, too! Sometimes the student who chose the rule doesn't realize that all the evidence needs to remain visible to the guessers. Help students establish a place to put the "don't fit" cards where everyone in the group can see them.

It's important that students deduce the Mystery Rule by examples, not by just guessing different rules. Only when it seems that most students have figured out the Mystery Rule, or when most of the cards have been placed, can they guess what the rule is. Then the rule-maker can turn over the secret word card to confirm it. Some students like to have all cards placed before the rule is revealed. Each student should have at least one turn (and if time allows, two turns) at choosing the Mystery Rule.

For some students, this game will be easy. However, this is the first time students will be playing "Guess My Rule" on their own in small groups. In addition to observing carefully the classification of the cards, they will also be struggling with turn-taking and—when it's their turn to choose the rule—managing others' guesses, giving accurate feedback, and deciding at what point players can guess the rule. For students who are just beginning to learn about small-group collaboration, this is all hard work. As you circulate, participate briefly in each game so that you can continue to model the need for careful observation of both positive and negative evidence. Where appropriate, help students decide on ways to manage their small-group work.

At this point, some students may invent the "double-rule" game that you will be introducing in the next session. By all means, encourage them to experiment with two rules if they seem ready to do so.

Extension: Using the computer for classification

Use the computer program *Gertrude's Secrets* (The Learning Company), which contains three types of classification games. The Loop Puzzles are a version of "Guess My Rule," using shape and color. No more than three students should work together at the computer; usually pairs are best so that each child can really participate. Some students might like to use the Shape Edit room, in which they can make their own shapes to use in the puzzles. They could try making some Yekttis, for example (although keep in mind that the new puzzle pieces can't be saved; they can be used only during the session in which they are created). ■

SESSION 3 ACTIVITIES

Introducing the two-rule version of "Guess My Rule"

Play "Guess My Rule" with students in the class, as you did in the first session of the investigation, *Sorting people: Who fits my rule?* You might want to start with one round of the game using a single rule to remind students how the game works.

Choose two rules such that some students will fit both (e.g., WEARING STRIPES and BROWN HAIR).

Now I have a bigger challenge. This time I have two Mystery Rules in mind. You'll be trying to figure out both of them. People who fit Rule 1 will stand over by the chalkboard. Sean and Amy fit my first rule. And I have another rule, a different one. Rule 2 people will stand by the windows. Jessica and Rosa fit Rule 2. This time when you choose someone, you have to tell me *which* rule you think the person fits.

As the game progresses, remind students to observe each group carefully and look for what the students in that group have in common.

At some point in the game, students will notice that some people belong in both groups. When this occurs (either during the game or once the rules have been guessed), ask them what they want to do about people who fit both rules (see the Dialogue Box,

Working with two rules, page 32). Usually, students suggest that these students go in the middle between the two walls or that they stand against a third wall. (If students do not bring up the overlap problem themselves, draw their attention to the issue of people who belong in both groups.)

When everyone has been assigned to the appropriate group, ask students to try to articulate a description for each group, including the group of students remaining in their seats. Not all students will be able to give precise descriptions; encourage them to give at least partial descriptions, and ask others to complete the description (as demonstrated in the Dialogue Box, *Working with two rules*).

Play one or two more rounds of "Guess My Rule" with people, this time using one of the class suggestions for where the students who fit both rules should stand.

Students enjoy contributing the rules for this game. You can have pairs or small groups of students each write down one possible Mystery Rule on an index card. Collect all the cards, mix them up, and draw out two. Use these two secret rules for the next round of the game. For some pairs of rules, you may have students who fit in the overlap group, but for other pairs—BROWN HAIR and BLACK HAIR, for example—there will be no students in both categories. ■

BROWN HAIR

BROWN HAIR
WEARING STRIPES

WEARING STRIPES

“”DIALOGUE BOX
Working with two rules

I'm thinking of one rule for people standing by the chalkboard [*the secret rule is BROWN HAIR*] and a different rule for people standing by the windows [*the secret rule is WEARING BLUE*]. I'll start out with Sean and Amy by the chalkboard, and I'm going to put Jessica and Rosa by the windows. Any ideas about who else might fit?

ALAN: I think Maya goes by the chalkboard.

Yes, she does fit there.

SERENA: Does Mark go by the windows?

No, he doesn't fit there.

SERENA: How about by the chalkboard?

Yes, Mark fits the rule I have for the group by the chalkboard. Who thinks they might know where Sam goes?

CARLOS: I don't think he goes in either place.

You're right, so what should Sam do?

CARLOS: He should just stay in his seat.

OK, Carlos is suggesting that Sam stay in his seat because he doesn't fit either rule. Does everyone agree?

LYNNE: Well, he should stand up.

Why should he do that?

LYNNE: Because then we'll remember that we already tried Sam and he didn't fit anywhere.

OK, so that's how we'll tell who doesn't fit.

[*Later*] . . .

I think you're ready to guess the rule for the people by the windows.

KIMARA: It's BLUE.

Yes, my rule was WEARING BLUE. OK, everyone who is wearing blue move over to the windows.

[*Several students from the "chalkboard group" start moving over to the windows.*]

[*Dramatically*] **But you're in the chalkboard group!**

[*They look confused. One of the students starts moving back.*]

[*Laughing*] **But you're in the BLUE group!**

SEVERAL STUDENTS [*talking at once*]: Wait a minute. I'm in both. Christina's got blue and she's in the chalkboard group. Yeah, and Maya has blue on her blouse, and she's in the chalkboard group, too.

Oh, dear, you're right. But Maya and Christina do fit my rule for the chalkboard group and they're WEARING BLUE. Let's see if we can get the rule for the chalkboard group and then we'll have to figure out what to do about people who fit both my rules. Does anyone think they know who else goes in the chalkboard group?

[*Later*] . . .

OK, you guessed that the chalkboard group all

have BROWN HAIR. Now, we have all these people who have BROWN HAIR over here, and all these people who are WEARING BLUE over there. But what can we do about the people who have BROWN HAIR *and* BLUE? They can't just keep running back and forth!

AMY: Well, all the people who have both could go to a different place.

EDDIE: They could stand over by the door.

JANE: They could go in the middle, like kind of touching both groups.

How would that work? . . .

[*Eventually all the students have been assigned to the chalkboard group (BROWN HAIR), the window group (WEARING BLUE), the middle group (BROWN HAIR AND WEARING BLUE), or are standing up at their seats (DON'T HAVE BROWN HAIR, NOT WEARING BLUE).*]

Now, who can tell me why some of you moved to the middle?

KATIE: Some of the kids with BROWN HAIR also had BLUE clothes on.

DENNIS: If you have both things, you stand in the middle. If you have one thing, you stand at the side.

Who could pick one of the groups and say exactly what the rule is for that group? And don't forget the group that is still at their seats—they're an important group, too!

LYNNE: Well, the chalkboard group has BROWN HAIR.

(Dialogue Box continued)

It's true, I see BROWN HAIR on everyone in the chalkboard group. But that's not the only place I see BROWN HAIR. Can anyone add to Lynne's description?

SAM: The middle group has BROWN HAIR, too.

Hmm, so how do I tell the difference?

LYNNE: The middle group has BROWN HAIR and they're WEARING BLUE.

ROSA: And the chalkboard group has BROWN HAIR and ISN'T WEARING BLUE!

What a clear way of putting it, Lynne and Rosa. Can anyone else describe one of the groups? How about the group still at their seats; that's a real challenge . . . ■

SESSION 4 ACTIVITIES

Introducing Venn diagrams: A way to show overlapping attributes

For information about the Venn diagrams you will be using in this session, see the Teacher Note, *Venn diagrams: Sorting by two attributes* (page 37). Have students gather around the floor or a table where you have placed the large sheet of paper with two *non-overlapping* circles on it.

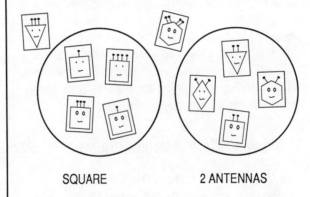

SQUARE   2 ANTENNAS

Choose two secret Yektti rules, one for each circle—for example, SQUARE and 2 ANTEN-NAS. Play "Guess My Rule" with two rules, using a small set of Yektti cards. Students have to specify in which circle they think a card belongs. Cards that do not fit either rule should also be placed in a visible space—for example, around the edges of the circles.

Once the rules have been determined by the group—or even during the game, since students have faced this issue in the

previous session—someone will bring up the problem of where to put Yekttis that fit both rules. Encourage any student suggestions about how to show clearly which Yekttis have both characteristics. For example, they could have a third circle that shows square Yekttis with 2 antennas; or they could put the cards that fit both rules down in such a way that they touch both circles.

After you have completed one game, display the large paper with two *overlapping* circles (or move your string or ribbon loops so that they overlap).

These overlapping circles make what we call *a Venn diagram*. You can use the fancy name for it, or you can call it a *circle diagram*. This is a kind of picture that mathematicians use to solve the problem of things that belong in both groups. The special place in the middle is really inside both circles, so that's where the Yekttis that are square *and* have 2 antennas can go. Which ones should we move to the middle?

SQUARE   2 ANTENNAS

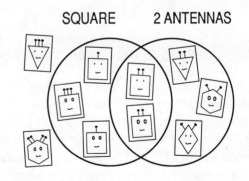

After they sort all the cards, ask students to describe what they see.

Which Yekttis can go only in Circle 1? How did you figure that out? Which can go only in Circle 2? When did you first suspect that was the rule? Which go in the middle? What kinds of Yekttis can't go in either of the two circles? [*Yekttis that are hexagons, triangles, and diamonds with 1, 3, or 4 antennas*] **How do you know?**

Keep in mind that many kinds of analytic skills are involved in this investigation. Some students will be able to *place* the Yekttis cards accurately, but may not be able to *verbalize* the descriptions of each group. Others may be able to describe the groups once they are formed, but may not be as good at using evidence during the course of the game. Students will learn from each other throughout these activities.

Try one or two more examples, using the intersecting circles, before students break up into their small groups.

Sorting by two rules: Small-group work

Students play "Guess My Rule" with two rules, using the large Venn diagrams you have prepared, the small Yekttis card set, and the Yekttis word cards. The rule-maker will choose *two* secret word cards, one for each circle. As you circulate, help the students remember that the middle section is really inside both circles and is the place for

Yekttis that fit *both* rules. If one circle is TRIANGLE and one is PLAIN EYES, Yekttis with triangle heads *and* plain eyes fit in the intersection. Sometimes, no Yekttis will fit in the middle. For example, if one rule is TRIANGLE and one rule is HEXAGON, no Yekttis are both. However, it is still perfectly legitimate to use these two rules.

Continue to circulate and support students as they become increasingly independent in managing their small-group work and thinking about these more difficult classification problems. Some students, using the large-group work as a model, will begin to discuss their strategies (see the Dialogue Box, *How did you know?*, on page 35). With your own questioning, encourage other students to begin to discuss how they are thinking about the problems.

Extension: More computer games

Use *Gertrude's Puzzles* (The Learning Company), a computer program that is a slightly more advanced version of *Gertrude's Secrets*. In particular, some students might want to try the 3-loop version of Loop Puzzles.

Extension: "Guess My Rule" with words

Using students' spelling words or any set of word cards, small groups can play "Guess My Rule" with words, using rules such as: HAS AN 'E', STARTS WITH AN 'S', HAS DOUBLE LETTERS, HAS TWO VOWELS, and so forth.

This game also works well as a chalkboard game with the whole group; it is a perfect fill-in activity for the few minutes before lunch or at the end of the school day.

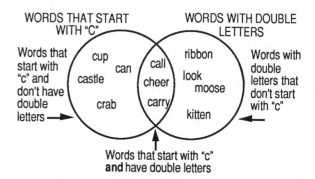

WORDS THAT START WITH "C"

WORDS WITH DOUBLE LETTERS

Words that start with "c" and don't have double letters →

cup
castle
can
crab

call
cheer
carry

ribbon
look
moose
kitten

← Words with double letters that don't start with "c"

Words that start with "c" **and** have double letters

Extension: Other attribute materials

See the Teacher Note, *Using the Yektti set* (page 29) for a discussion of appropriate attribute materials to use for further classification activities.

Extension: Yektti stories and pictures

Many classes have integrated this mathematics activity with writing and art. Since only the Yekttis' heads have been seen, it is anybody's guess what their bodies look like. According to the Yektti story, Lee did learn to communicate with the Yekttis a little, but their language was very strange and difficult, so he couldn't ask a lot of the questions he wanted to ask. For instance, he never found out why they never came out of the holes in the ground or what the rest of their bodies looked like. Students can draw pictures of what they think a complete Yektti might look like and/or write stories about Yektti culture and habits: What do they eat? Do they work? If so, doing what? Do they live in families? What do they do for fun? What is their home planet like? Students have really enjoyed this activity and have come up with many wonderful descriptions of Yekttis. (See the Dialogue Box, *Second graders describe Yekttis*, page 36). ■

❝❞DIALOGUE BOX
How did you know?

[*Working in a small group with Amy, Tony, and Lena, Glenn has picked two secret Yektti rules:* RINGED EYES *and* TRIANGLE *heads.*]

AMY [*choosing* 4 ANTENNAS, RINGED EYES, SQUARE]: Does this fit the rule?

GLENN: Yes, it goes here.

TONY [*picking* 4 ANTENNAS, RINGED EYES, HEXAGON]: This one?

GLENN: Yup.

TONY: Oh, it could be two of one, I mean one of two. They both have DOUGHNUT EYES and they both have 4 ANTENNAS.

LENA: [*holding up* 4 ANTENNAS, RINGED EYES, DIAMOND]: This one goes.

TONY: But it could still be both.

AMY: [*showing* 4 ANTENNAS, PLAIN EYES, DIAMOND]: I know! This one!

GLENN: No, it's a reject. Good information!

[*Tony silently holds up a* 3 ANTENNAS, RINGED EYES, DIAMOND *Yektti.*]

GLENN: It fits.

AMY: Can I guess it? [*Glenn nods.*] It's RINGED EYES.

LENA: How did you know?

AMY: I looked over here [*indicates the discards*] and I saw there were no RINGED EYES.

TONY: At first I thought it was 4 ANTENNAS, but that one [*points to* 4 ANTENNAS, PLAIN EYES] didn't go, so I changed my mind.

LENA: This is good. You got it after 11 cards.

GLENN: But you don't know my other rule yet. ■

Yekttis: What has a square head, one antenna, and doughnut eyes?   **35**

66 99 DIALOGUE BOX
Second graders describe Yekttis

Here are some Yektti descriptions from second graders—in their own words and spellings!

▼ Yekttis eat a strange kind of food. It is called mingilems. It is different colors. They live on a place cold and damp. No scientists know what it is called but I do. It is called Otulp. My Yektti's name is Rocky. The End.

▼ My Yektti's name is Mimi. It lives on a different planet that is far away. She only eats salad. She is a princess. On her planet they play nentendo for fun. They get electriede from there antenas. She has fore antenas. All yekktis are peceful.

▼ Yekttis eat rats and mice braens. The yekttis had a queen but she died. When she died they wood not lison to the king so they went by there on rules. And thats the end of the story. ■

✎ TEACHER NOTE
Venn diagrams: Sorting by two attributes

To introduce Venn diagrams, we deliberately begin with two circles that are not overlapping so that students get a chance to think about two rules at a time and to invent ways of dealing with items that fit in both categories.

Suppose we are sorting animals according to two categories: ANIMALS THAT LIVE IN OUR NEIGHBORHOOD and ANIMALS THAT CAN HOP. We might think of these animals:

LIVE IN THE
NEIGHBORHOOD   HOP

We soon realize that some of the animals fit in both circles. Suppose that in our neighborhood, for example, there aren't any rabbits or kangaroos, but there are grasshoppers and frogs. We could write these animals in both circles, or we might place them in a separate spot, say above and between the two circles.

However, mathematicians have a way of representing the data that clearly shows the relationship between the two categories. By moving the two circles together, we create an overlapping space that is inside *both* circles. Now we can see that some animals fit in only one circle, some fit in only the other circle, and some fit in both:

LIVE IN THE   HOP
NEIGHBORHOOD

The word AND is important in describing the space inside the two circles, which we might call the *overlap* or *intersection*. The grasshopper and frog hop AND live in our neighborhood. The animals in the left-hand circle live in our neighborhood but do not hop. The animals in the right-hand circle hop but do not live in our neighborhood.

Some teachers emphasize the separate categories by drawing the two circles in different colors or making them with two different colors of ribbon or string. Color provides an easier way to identify each circle: *Does this one fit in the yellow circle? Are you*

ready to guess the rule for the blue circle? Everything in the yellow circle has 2 antennas. It also may help some students visually isolate each circle, and see that the intersection is inside both circles.

Of course, even though a space exists to show items that fit in both categories, there may not be any items that fit in both. For example, if our two categories are STUDENTS WITH BROWN EYES and STUDENTS WITH BLUE EYES, we will not have students who fit both criteria. This situation will come up in using the Yekttis when students select two word cards, such as SQUARE and HEXAGON—that describe two mutually exclusive categories. That is, no Yektti has a square head AND a hexagon head.

This situation might also arise in classifying real data. Suppose we are classifying animals in two categories: animals that LIVE IN OUR NEIGHBORHOOD and animals that SWIM. In one community there might be no animals that fit in the intersection:

LIVE IN THE   SWIM
NEIGHBORHOOD

In another community, there might be many
animals that fit in the intersection:

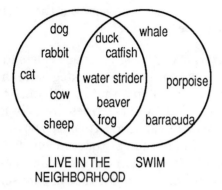

In this second case, the duck, catfish, water
strider, beaver, and frog all live in the neighborhood AND swim. ∎

Sorting: Groups and Graphs

PART 2
Sorting and classifying data

"THING COLLECTIONS": WHAT GOES WITH WHAT?

INVESTIGATION OVERVIEW

What happens

In this investigation, students explore physical attributes of common objects, including both properties they can see and feel, such as what the object is made of, and properties that they can discover only through experiment and observation—for example, whether something floats in water. This investigation can be easily integrated with the science curriculum, and you may want to add some additional experiments in line with science activities you are planning (see page 52 for some suggestions).*

In this investigation, students collect data about a "thing collection," consisting of

---

*The development of this investigation was influenced by one of the Elementary Science Study units, *Sink or Float*, which the authors used in their own classrooms. For further work in this area, you may want to use the unit itself, which is available from Delta Education, Inc., P.O. Box M, Nashua, NH 03061-6012. A related unit, *Clay Boats*, is also available from Delta.

everyday objects; they then represent their findings using Venn diagrams, tables, pictures, and graphs. In the first two sessions, they devise their own criteria for sorting the objects according to properties they can see. In the last two sessions, students experiment to see whether objects sink or float in water.

The activities take four classes of about 45 minutes each.

What to plan ahead of time

▼ Prepare identical "thing collections" of about 20 small objects—one collection for each group of 3 students and an extra for yourself (Sessions 1–4). See the Teacher Note, *Preparing a "thing collection,"* page 43, for specific suggestions.

▼ Duplicate the one-circle diagram (page 80) for each group of 3 students (Sessions 1–2).

▼ Make a transparency similar to the one-circle diagram for use with an overhead projector (optional, Session 1).

▼ Duplicate the two-circle diagram (page 81) for each group of 3 students (optional, Session 2).

▼ Set up a small tub or basin half-filled with water for each group of 2–3 students (Session 3). Plastic dishwashing tubs work well. You may be able to borrow the tubs from the science teacher or the kindergarten, or students may be able to bring them from home. The tubs should be on a surface that can get wet and be wiped off later. Spread newspaper on the floor under the area if you wish.

▼ For objects in the collection that are likely to disintegrate or get waterlogged (such as an index card), have extras available so students will be able to try these items more than once (Session 3).

▼ Prepare and duplicate a recording sheet for each small group, with the things in the collection listed down the left side and space to write next to them (Session 3).

| Popsicle stick |
| nail |
| paper clip |
| candle |
| index card |
| button |
| string |
| |

Important mathematical ideas

Thinking flexibly about the characteristics of the data. The "thing collections" make up a complex set with many characteristics. As students sort the materials themselves or try to figure out how others have sorted them, they must think about the objects in many different ways, shifting their points of view in order to see relationships that may not be immediately obvious.

Articulating logical reasoning. As students gain experience with developing and defining categories, ask them more often to explain how they came to a decision, to substantiate their conjectures, and to give reasons for their ideas, as shown in the Dialogue Box, *Paying attention to the evidence.*

Constructing clear definitions for "fuzzy" attributes. Many of the characteristics students have encountered so far in the unit have been relatively easy to define, although you have probably already run into some difficulties in definition—for example, is a student's hair brown or blond or in-between? The collections are more like real-world data, which are often "messy" and hard to define. Is a rubber band *round*? Well, sometimes. Is a nail *tall* or *short*? It depends.

In this investigation, students grapple with the challenges of being precise, clear, and accurate in describing categorical data, as discussed in the Teacher Note, *The challenge of fuzzy attributes: The teacher's role.*

Constructing your own categories to describe the data. In the sink-or-float section of this investigation, students construct their own categories to describe data they have collected. Important categories may not always be known ahead of time, *before* data collection and analysis, but may emerge through experimentation or observation. As students learn more about their data, they often see new ways of sorting that they did not consider earlier—a process described in the Teacher Note, *Constructing your own categories.*

Inventing representations of data. At this age level, students are encouraged to come up with their own ideas for pictures, sketches, tables, and graphs to portray their findings, as illustrated in the Teacher Note, *Inventing pictures of the data.*

Using more than one representation to view data. Again, students have the opportunity to see their peers graph the same data in different ways. In the process, they pick up new ideas about picturing data and begin to see how different representations can communicate different information.

Building theories about the data. Collecting, representing, and thinking about data lead to many descriptions of and theories about the world. Even young children can *use* their data as a basis for conjecturing, describing, generalizing, and wondering. ■

✎ TEACHER NOTE
Preparing a "thing collection"

Collections of common objects give students the chance to explore similarities and differences in shape, color, texture, material, function, and a variety of other properties. Following are a few guidelines for putting together classroom "thing collections."

▼ A collection of about 20 small objects provides enough variety and is a manageable size for second and third graders.

▼ As you choose objects, look for a few clear properties that are each shared by 4–8 objects. For example, you might include 7 ROUND things, 5 RED things, 6 METAL things, and 4 PLASTIC things. Of course, some objects might have more than one of these characteristics.

▼ Try to avoid too much variety in color so students will focus on other properties.

▼ You will need some objects that will sink and some that will float in water. Also include a few things that float for a while, then sink once they become waterlogged (index card), or things that sometimes sink, and sometimes float, depending on how you put them into the water (paper cup).

▼ Because you will be playing "Guess My Rule" with the whole class, and each small group will be using its own collection, all the collections should be identical. For instance, if you include pipe cleaners, put the same colors in each collection. If you include paper clips, use the same size for everyone.

▼ Store each collection in a small plastic refrigerator container or plastic bag. (Sometimes students count the container as part of the collection, too.)

▼ You may want to exclude things that roll easily (like marbles) because they are hard to sort on flat surfaces.

▼ Keep a supply of duplicate objects, as some will inevitably be lost or broken, or will disintegrate when put in water in Session 3.

You will probably have your own ideas for suitable objects that are readily available. A list of suggested items is given at right. ■

index card	straw
pipe cleaner	rubber band
button	piece of string
small paper clip	peanut (in the shell)
large paper clip	sugar cube
red checker	piece of bric-a-brac
black checker	plastic drink stirrer
jack	Unifix cube (or centi-
key	meter cube)
screw	Popsicle stick (or
toothpick	tongue depressor)
nail	wooden bead
birthday candle	piece of aluminum foil
piece of sponge	plastic coffee can lid
paper cup	poker chip
piece of macaroni	penny

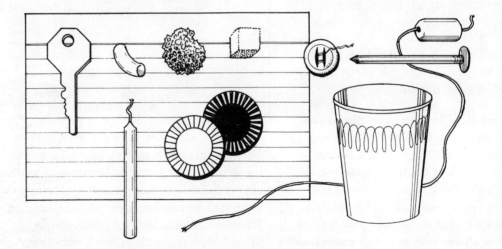

SESSION 1 ACTIVITIES

Describing and recording data: Exploring the collections

Give one "thing collection" to each group of three students. Allow time for them to look through their materials. Encourage students to touch, look closely, count, sort, or use any other mode of exploration. Many groups will be able to manage their own exploration. For any group that needs help focusing, suggest one of the following:

1. After everyone has had a chance to look carefully at the materials, one student holds the collection in its container on his or her lap (out of sight) while the others try to name as many objects in the collection as they can.

2. With the collection in sight, play "Twenty Questions" to guess which object one student has in mind.

Students need about 5 minutes to explore their collections before you ask them to focus on a large-group discussion.

You've been learning to look carefully as you think about what's the same and what's different in a group of things. You did this when we played "Guess My Rule" with the class and with the Yekttis. Now let's do the same with our "thing collections." What can you tell me about what's the same and what's different about all the things in the collection?

Encourage students to make statements about the whole collection, not just about individual objects (see the Teacher Note, *Making generalizations about a collection*, page 46). Quickly record their descriptions of the collections and organize their information in a chart like one of those shown here.

This collection does:	This collection does not:
Have 20 objects	Have anything alive
Have some shiny things	Have anything green . . .
Have a lot of small things	

Everything in the collection:	is metal, plastic, or paper is smaller than a chalkboard eraser is larger than . . .
Nothing in the collection:	is alive can be eaten is gold or silver . . .
Some things in the collection:	are white are round you can write on are useful . . .

This discussion is simply an introduction to the collections, giving students a chance to observe carefully and to use and hear a variety of words that describe the objects. The discussion need not go on too long—probably no more than 5–10 minutes.

Organizing the collections: Playing "Guess My Rule"

We're going to play "Guess My Rule" with the collections. It will probably be harder now than when we played it with the Yekttis, because there are a lot more possible rules. You'll have to look very carefully at the evidence. Don't jump to conclusions. I want you to be able to give good reasons for your ideas.

Give each group a copy of the one-circle diagram, page 80. If you are using an overhead projector, put your own transparency with one circle on the projector.

This is a one-circle diagram. We're going to play with just one rule at a time today. When we identify an object that fits the rule, put it inside your circle. When we find an object that doesn't fit, put it outside the circle so you can see which things don't fit the rule.

Depending on the things in your collections, a good beginning Mystery Rule may be ROUND. Start the students off by telling them one or two objects that go inside the circle and one or two that belong outside the circle. (If you have an overhead projector, place the objects appropriately.) As objects that fit or don't fit are identified, have the small groups follow along, using their own collections and circle diagrams. (Even if you are using the overhead projector, students will have to look at their own collections, too, because not all features will show up clearly on the overhead projection.)

As students make guesses, challenge them to consider all the evidence, both negative and positive. Since students now have quite a lot of experience with the "Guess My Rule" game, you no longer need to accept all conjectures as equally legitimate. Begin to ask students to give reasons for their ideas (see the Dialogue Box, *Paying attention to the evidence,* following, and the Teacher Note, *Mathematical discussions: Challenging ideas,* page 47).

Play the game one more time, perhaps using METAL or PAPER as your rule.

Describing the collections: Small-group work

Students now play "Guess My Rule" in small groups, using the "thing collections" and the one-circle diagrams. Circulate to help students clarify the rules they are using and to encourage them to find words that accurately describe their rule. ■

---

66 99 DIALOGUE BOX
Paying attention to the evidence

The teacher's Mystery Rule is THINGS THAT HAVE A POINT. The students have already guessed that a pencil, a nail, a jack, a paper clip, and a plastic stirrer do fit the rule and that all other objects in the collection do not fit. Students are trying to figure out what the rule is.

EDDIE [*waving his hand wildly*]: I know. I know!

What do you think, Eddie?

EDDIE: It's METAL, things that are metal.

What's your evidence for that?

EDDIE: What?

How can you prove to us that the rule is THINGS THAT ARE METAL?

EDDIE: Well, the nail and the jack and the paper clip...

JANE: It can't be METAL because...

Wait, Jane, because I want to hear Eddie's thinking about this. How were you thinking about it?

EDDIE: Well, I was thinking the nail and the paper clip were metal . . . [*Stops, looks uncomfortable.*]

Uh-huh. And do you want to revise your

thinking at all?

EDDIE: Well, it can't be METAL because the pencil isn't metal.

Good evidence. Does anyone else see evidence to support Eddie's conclusion that THINGS THAT ARE METAL can't be the rule?

JANE: And the plastic stick isn't metal.

OK. My rule wasn't METAL. Any more ideas? This is a hard one. Tell me even if you had a good idea that you decided wasn't the rule. Did anyone have an idea they decided didn't work?

ELISABETH: Well, I was thinking LONG until someone guessed the jack, and that's not long.

So you really used that clue. If I take the jack away, can anyone see a good reason why LONG still isn't the rule?

MARK: Yeah, the Popsicle stick isn't in the circle, and that's long.

OK, so Mark used evidence from the things that *don't* fit my rule. Remember, that's important evidence. Who else is thinking about a rule that might work?

Lena: It's, like, DIFFERENT SHAPES.

Tell us how you're thinking that DIFFERENT SHAPES works?

LENA: Well, like, the paper clip is like that [*shows the shape in the air*] and the jack is like a star.

And what did you think about the nail?

(Dialogue Box continued)

LENA: It's straight.

Uh-huh. And did they all go together somehow?

LENA: Yeah, they're, like, SHAPES.

Kimara?

KIMARA: Well, it can't be SHAPES because the bead and the checker and the Popsicle stick are all shapes and they don't fit.

Kimara thinks that SHAPES doesn't work because there are some shapes that don't fit my rule. Other ideas?

AMY: Not exactly LONG, but kind of LONG AND POINTY.

How would LONG AND POINTY work for the things in the circle?

👉 In this discussion the teacher begins to require that students give good reasons for their ideas, rather than make unsubstantiated guesses. She has noticed that Eddie tends to guess quickly and impulsively, considering only one or two of the objects. She is sure he can make a more reasoned guess if challenged to do so. Lena, on the other hand, seems genuinely confused about how to make a general statement about the objects. Her overly inclusive category of SHAPES is a common approach used by primary grade students who are still developing an understanding of classification. Kimara's comment may help clarify why SHAPES does not work, but Lena may not be ready to take in this explanation. She needs continued experience in classification activities.

The teacher is careful not to challenge students only when she thinks they are "wrong"; rather, she asks students to explain their thinking as often as possible, so that she communicates her interest in how they are thinking, not just in getting the correct answer. ∎

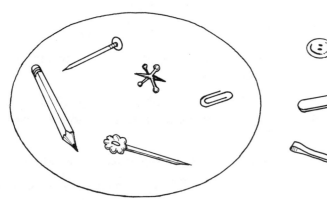

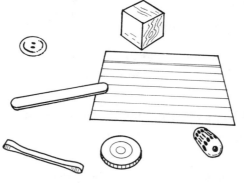

Making generalizations about a "thing collection"

Looking at a "thing collection" as a whole is a difficult task for many second and third graders. Students at this level are often more used to focusing on individual objects and individual characteristics. However, at this point in the unit, they have had some good experience in making generalizations about a group by focusing on one particular characteristic and ignoring others. For example, when they played "Guess My Rule" with the class, they described one group as WEARING BLUE and ignored everything else that was different about the individuals in that group.

Teachers have found that it is sometimes a bit hard to get the initial discussion going. Once students have heard a few examples, though, they quickly catch on to the idea of making general statements about the collection. For example, characteristics of the collections that students have noticed include:

Some of it is little and some of it is big.
Most of it isn't made out of paper.
There are some things you can stir with.
Some things have spirals.
They're not alive.
Nothing is gold.
You can see through some of the things.

Of course, the particular characteristics your students see may be different, depending on the objects in your collection.

As students offer their generalizations, encourage them to clarify what they mean. For instance, one student's remark that "you can see through some things" prompted a discussion of what she meant by "see through." As it turned out, she meant *transparent,* but some students pointed out that they could "see through" a wooden bead in the collection because it had a hole in the middle.

When another student suggested that "most of it isn't made out of paper," the teacher asked her to clarify what she meant by "most." The students found that three objects (out of 20) were made of paper and agreed that, therefore, "most" objects were not paper. Another student suggested that "some are big and some are small," and the teacher asked everyone to talk about which objects they would call big or small and why.

You will certainly have your own ideas about how *you* would describe the collection. However, it is more important that students clarify their *own* thinking and express their *own* ideas precisely, than that they agree with your personal descriptions. ■

✎ TEACHER NOTE
Mathematical discussions: Challenging ideas

One of the most important ideas in mathematics is that one's assertions should be subject to scrutiny and challenge. The history of mathematics is the history of debate and discussion, yet we do not see much discussion in most mathematics classes.

In fact, many students are convinced that there is always one right answer and one "best" procedure in mathematics class. This idea often leads them to be nervous if their answers or strategies seem to conflict. But discussion about different strategies, different approaches, and different solutions lies at the heart of mathematics. Encouraging students to make assertions, to base their arguments on data, to state their reasons, and to ask others clarifying questions is a vital aspect of teaching mathematics.

Challenging students' ideas is a delicate matter, yet it can be a very effective way of probing to find out what your students are thinking and to help them clarify and extend their own ideas. Many teachers find that the best way of examining students' ideas is to ask questions that invite them to explain their reasons:

Say more about that. . . . Can you give me an example? . . . How do the data tell you that?

Another technique is to ask students to relate their ideas to other students' ideas:

Is this like Serena's idea? . . . Are your reasons the same as Eddie's? . . . Lynne's theory and Glenn's are very different. Could they both work? What evidence that would help us know if either of these theories work?

A third way teachers sometimes probe students' ideas is to give counter-examples or suggest thought experiments:

Some other second [third] graders say that heavy things always sink. What would you tell them? . . . Do you think anything would change if we collected more data from other second graders? . . . Do you think if we did the same survey again today, the results would be the same as the one we did yesterday?

You may have other techniques that work for you. Once ideas are flowing, you may find that the students themselves make many suggestions, ask each other probing questions, and help to formulate ideas. Until then, however, it is important to keep discussion alive. Researchers have found that simply waiting 3 seconds after asking a question gives students time to organize their thinking and to develop some of their ideas before answering. Three seconds seems like a very long time when you're used to much faster answers, but students need to feel that they have time to think. Hurrying them to an answer defeats the whole purpose of mathematical discussions. ■

SESSION 2 ACTIVITIES

More observation and description: Constructing rules for sorting

Each small group picks a Mystery Rule about their "thing collection" to challenge the rest of the class in "Guess My Rule." Before making this challenge, each group writes down their rule and sorts their collection according to that rule. This process will help each group clearly define their rule.

If you have an overhead projector, students enjoy using it with the one-circle transparency as the other groups follow along with their own collections. As in the previous session, challenge students to clarify and defend their conjectures. This investigation provides many opportunities for language experience and enriching vocabulary (see the Teacher Note: *Using fancy words*, page 49).

As students try to guess each other's Mystery Rules, you will notice some of the difficulties inherent in describing a real-world collection with so many different attributes (see the Teacher Note, *The challenge of fuzzy attributes*, page 49). It is appropriate for students to struggle with these difficulties; they are real problems that come up in describing real data. Continue to encourage students to refer to the characteristics of the objects for evidence.

Alternative scheduling: Some students

have more trouble staying focused in the large group than in their small groups. For this game, you may want to cover only one or two Mystery Rules at a time, spacing the activity out over a day or two rather than hearing from all the small groups in one session.

Extension: *Double-rule "Guess My Rule"*

Students can play "Guess My Rule" in their small groups, using two rules with the collections. Page 81 provides a Venn diagram with two overlapping circles for this game. Because the "thing collections," unlike the Yekttis, can be sorted in so many different ways, double-rule "Guess My Rule" with the collections can be quite challenging. As students play, help them keep in mind that one rule applies to Circle 1, the second rule to Circle 2, and that objects in the intersection are in both circles and, therefore, must fit both rules. The rule-maker should write down the two Mystery Rules on index cards or scraps of paper and place them facedown near the two circles before the game begins. This activity is excellent for small-group independent work or for a learning center.

Extension: *Students' own collections*

Take a survey: What do you collect? You may be surprised how many students collect things. In one classroom of 18 students, there were 19 different collections!

Students who have collections at home can bring them in to share, display them, write about them, sort them, and represent them. Students who don't have collections might be able to work with friends who do.

Extension: *Making classroom collections*

Each pair or small group can create their own collection of objects based on a characteristic they choose. Students have chosen such attributes as THINGS MADE OUT OF METAL, THINGS THAT ARE RED, JUNK FOOD, and THINGS YOU CAN'T BREAK.

An alternative is to pick one or two attributes for which the whole class brings in objects. The attributes might relate to some other area of study—for example, THINGS THAT CAN BE PICKED UP BY A MAGNET, THINGS THAT USED TO BE ALIVE, THINGS THAT DON'T COME FROM THE UNITED STATES, THINGS THAT BIRDS WILL EAT.

Even simple attributes can be interesting. One classroom brought in THINGS THAT ARE BLUE, and made a beautiful display of objects with an amazing range of blues Even here, definition and description were challenging: Do we all agree on what is blue? Does "blue" include "purple"? When does blue shade off into green? What are other words that describe some shade of blue? ■

✎ TEACHER NOTE
Using fancy words

This investigation is a particularly good one for integrating language experience and vocabulary development into mathematics. As students struggle to describe the characteristics of their collections, they hear new words from other students, and you can find opportunities to introduce other words that are appropriate to the conversation. Students in the primary grades enjoy learning and using "fancy words" when they are embedded in some compelling experience rather than isolated as vocabulary words to be memorized.

For example, one student said that some objects were "like glass." Once the teacher clarified what the student meant, she introduced the word *transparent* into the conversation ("Oh, you mean it's *transparent*, you can see right through it?")—not insisting that students use this word, but simply adding it to the vocabulary they were hearing. Not surprisingly, many students began to use the word as they continued the investigation.

A small group that chose "things that are halfway to a circle" (including a paper clip and a Popsicle stick) expressed beautifully, using words they understood, the idea of "semicircular." The teacher acknowledged the students' definition by repeating their wording, and also offered them new vocabulary: "Oh, things that are halfway to a circle, I see exactly what you mean. There's a half circle—you can call it a semicircle—right here on the paper clip, and there are semicircles on the ends of the Popsicle stick."

Malleable, unbreakable, and *opaque* are other "fancy" words that have surfaced in classrooms during this investigation. ∎

✎ TEACHER NOTE
The challenge of fuzzy attributes: The teacher's role

Work with the "thing collections" is quite different from work with the Yekttis. The "thing collections" provide experience with the real problems that arise in classifying data. As in many other real-world data sets, the number of different attributes of objects in the collections is almost limitless. Further, many of the attributes are "fuzzy," not as easy to define clearly as those of the Yekttis. There is no disagreement about whether a Yektti has one or two antennas, but there is much room for discussion about which objects in the collection are USEFUL or SMALL or LONG. For example, some of the rules students have invented include:

things you can tie

things that are halfway to a circle [they have a semicircular part]

things that are "up"

things that have swirls

things that are long

All these rules lead to legitimate problems of definition and clarification. Such issues should not be simplified for the students, because these are exactly the ideas that can stimulate deeper thinking about classification. In particular, three issues often arise as students of this age work on sorting:

▼ **A category can be "seen," but is very difficult to describe.** For example, the students whose rule was THINGS THAT ARE UP used a birthday candle and a nail standing vertically, on their ends, to illustrate their rule. They also chose a large wooden bead and a checker. A paper clip, paper price tag, and index card did not fit their rule. Their concept seemed to be something like "objects with a discernible height." They had constructed a legitimate "fuzzy" characteristic, hard to define yet real. Other students seemed to know what they meant, too; one student, attempting to guess the rule, said "They're puffy." It is very tempting to "help" students with such an idea by getting them to substitute a simpler rule, one that is not so hard to define (for example, leave out the bead and the checker and call the category TALL AND THIN). Instead, help students clarify their rule simply by asking them what does and does not belong in their category and why.

▼ **Some descriptions require a basis for comparison.** For example, the students who chose THINGS THAT ARE LONG had not really thought about what they meant by this relative term. When they began to field other students' guesses, they found they could not really agree on which objects did and did not fit their rule. Although the situation is dif-ferent, the teacher's role is very similar to that described above: that is, ask students, *before* they challenge the rest of the class, to decide which objects fit their rule, which objects don't fit, and why. Challenge their choices and help them verbalize their reasons.

Students at this age need a great deal of experience with the comparison implicit in measurement terms like *long, heavy, big, far, tall,* or *warm.* What dimension is being considered? What is being compared to what? Even a measurement that seems exact may require further definition. One small group made their own collection of THINGS THAT ARE 2 INCHES LONG. When they found that hardly anything was exactly that length, they decided that anything between 1-1/2 and 2-1/2 inches was close enough.

▼ **Different words can describe the same characteristic.** The group whose rule was THINGS THAT HAVE SWIRLS did not accept student guesses of "things that are kind of like stairs, that are down and up, down and up" or "things that are zigzag." There was outraged protest when they announced their rule because other students felt they had already identified the category in differ-ent words. The teacher helped both the student guessers and the student rule-makers explore whether or not their definitions were really different. In this case, the rule-makers presented a good case that while *zigzags* and *stairs* had corners, *swirls* (like on a birthday can-dle and a screw) were curvy. In such a case, the teacher must, on the one hand, encourage the clarification of real differences in definition and, on the other hand, discourage students from being too rigid about guesses. If other students have guessed the concept and have accurately described the character-istics of the category, the exact word should not be at issue. ■

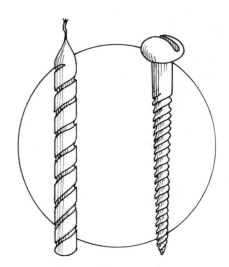

SESSION 3 AND 4 ACTIVITIES

This part of the investigation requires two class sessions, which can be split up in different ways. The sink and float experiment itself requires 20–25 minutes. If you have only 45 minutes, you could use Session 3 for the experiment, clean-up, and a class discussion about what students found out. Then, students can represent and write about the data in Session 4.

If you can devote an hour to the first of the two sessions, students can begin drawing and writing in Session 3, then finish this work and have a whole-class discussion in Session 4. The advantage of this second sequence is that students begin writing and recording right after their experimenting.

Collecting and recording data: What floats? What sinks?

Today we're going to collect some data about your "thing collections" by doing an experiment. This time, we're going to try to find out something about these objects that you may not be able to tell just by looking at them.

Your job today is to find out which of these sink and which float. Find out as much as you can about each object. Does it always sink? Does it always float? Does anything else happen to it?

Each group of two or three students needs a "thing collection," a basin of water, and the recording sheet you have prepared. If your students are not used to water activities, you may want to establish some guidelines (e.g., no splashing). However, since this activity is usually quite absorbing for students of this age, it is best to tolerate a bit of spillage—some water is bound to get on the surrounding surfaces—as long as the activity remains productive.

Ask students to test the objects carefully, one at a time, and write down what they find out for each object on the recording sheet. Their notes can be rough—for example, some students write *F* and *S* for *float* and *sink*—but should include as much information as possible.

As you circulate in the classroom during this experiment, encourage students to move beyond the simple categories of FLOAT and SINK as they find out more about the objects. For example, sometimes students notice that certain objects (such as an index card) will float for a while and then sink; others (such as a paper cup) will sometimes float and sometimes sink, depending on how they are placed in the water. Depending on what you have in the collections, some objects may get soggy or disintegrate when left in the water. Many students will notice other characteristics as well.

Organizing the data: Inventing representations

When scientists do an experiment, they need to communicate to other people what they found out from the experiment. Often they use graphs and pictures to show what happened.

For the experiment you just did, each group is going to invent some pictures or graphs that will show other people what you found out that was interesting and important. Most of you found out which objects float and which sink, and some of you found out some other things, too. Use your list to help you think about what you found out about the objects in your collection.

Each group needs to decide how they want to show their data. As in the earlier investigation, *Sorting people: Who fits my rule?*, encourage each group to use more than one way of showing what they found. Different students in the same group can make different representations of their findings. Emphasize the value of looking at the data in more than one way (see the Teacher Note, *Inventing pictures of the data*, page 54).

When students have ideas that lead beyond the original two categories of FLOAT and SINK, encourage them to create and name additional categories for their graphs or pictures. This process of deciding what categories are needed to convey the best information about the data is one of the key ideas in this unit (see the Teacher Note, *Constructing your own categories*, page 55).

Interpreting the data and developing theories: Why do some things sink and some things float?

A class discussion focused on why some things sunk and others floated is a good way to bring this investigation to an end. Students will probably have begun talking about their theories during their small-group work. The object of this discussion is not for your second or third graders to completely grasp the reasons for objects' sinking and floating, but rather for them to develop and test their own ideas by referring to the evidence they have collected. As in their work with "Guess My Rule," they will need to pay attention to both positive and negative evidence. For example, if one theory is that heavier things sink, then this theory can be tested through positive examples (Do heavy things sink?) *and* through negative ones (Do light things *not* sink?). See the Dialogue Box, *Second graders' theories about sinking and floating*, for excerpts from the concluding discussion in one classroom (page 53).

Publishing results

After the class discussion, ask each student to write a few sentences describing the results of their experiment; or, as part of your language experience work, meet with each small group and ask them to dictate to you what was most interesting or surprising about their work with sinking and floating.

This investigation gives students an opportunity to "publish" the results of their data collection and analysis. Publishing is one of the phases in the data analysis process, just as in the writing process (see the Teacher Note, *Phases of data analysis: Learning from the process approach to writing*, page 75). For students at this age level, it is usually not particularly useful to have each group show their graphs and report to the rest of the class. Students' oral reports rarely reflect the quality of the thinking that has gone into their work, and it is hard for the class to be attentive through a series of seven or eight similar reports. However, it can be very effective to publish students' writing and their representations as an attractive bulletin board display, or as a book for the class library.

Extension: More science experiments

A wonderful task for a second sink-and-float session comes from the Elementary Science Study unit on sinking and floating (see the note on page 41): Take one of the things that floats and find a way to make it sink; then take one of the things that sinks and find a way to make it float.

What other properties of the "thing collections" can be discovered through experimentation, observation, and recording? You may have some ideas that fit with your science curriculum, and students can also brainstorm their own ideas for experimentation. A sequence similar to the one suggested for these sessions on sinking and floating can be followed to explore such questions as: Which objects are heavy and which are light? Which objects are attracted to a magnet? Which objects conduct electricity? ■

"" DIALOGUE BOX
Second graders' theories about sinking and floating

Do you have any ideas now about why some things sink and some things float? Did anything surprise you? Did some things you thought would sink float and some things you thought would float sink?

PAUL: Anything with an air pocket or plastic or foam will float.

JESSICA: The screw does sink because it was heavy, it was made out of metal.

So, we have two ideas, one reason why some things floated and one reason why something sank.

SERENA: Because heavy stuff sinks and light stuff floats.

What does she mean by heavy?

CARLOS: It sinks to the ground, heavy.

LENA: You can feel it.

SEAN: I don't agree about heavy things sinking.

Why not, Sean?

SEAN: Not all stuff that's heavy sinks cause the plastic box, we put that in, and it didn't sink.

ELISABETH: Yeah, and we even put things in it. We put in the screw, and it still didn't sink!

Can anyone else think of any evidence about this? Do light things float and heavy things sink?

EDDIE: I don't sink. I can float on the water and stay up.

AMY: Once I was in a big pond and I picked up a rock and it made me sink.

Can you think of anything else heavy, not something in the classroom, that floats?

DENNIS: A boat.

JANE: A boat can sink or float.

A boat sinks?

JANE: If there's a hole in it, there's a shipwreck.

KATIE: The water goes into it and pushes it down.

So the water can push it down? Hmmm. So what are you all thinking now about whether heavy things sink and light things float?

BILLY: It doesn't matter how heavy or light it is.

GLENN: Because a heavy thing might be able to swim or lay on the water.

And are there any light things that sank when you tried them?

TONY: Yeah, the paper clip sank.

CHRISTINA: And the index card. The water went over it and pushed it down.

Any other ideas about why some of the things you tried sank and why some things floated?

MAYA: Because of the water skin.

The water skin?

MAYA: Like the plastic stick, the stirrer. Sometimes it floated if you put it down real carefully because the water skin holds it up, and if you push it under the water, it will just sink.

So sometimes something floated because the water skin held it up? Who has another one that floated and can tell us a reason—the same one as Maya's or a different one—why they think it floated?

LYNNE: The plastic container because of the air. If it has air in it, it floats. But if it doesn't have air in it, it can't float.

TONY: And the Styrofoam ball. It has more air in it than the screw or the paper clip, so it floats.

That is like what Paul said at the beginning about an air pocket. Are there other things you can think of that have air in them? ∎

✎ TEACHER NOTE
Inventing pictures of the data

When students invent their own individual ways of representing their data, they often come up with wonderful pictures or graphs that powerfully communicate the meaning of the data. While many commonly used representations, such as bar graphs, tables, line plots, and tallies, should gradually become familiar to students (see the Teacher Note, *Sketching data*, page 24), we want to encourage students to use their own inventiveness and creativity to develop pictures and graphs as well. In this way, students make the data their own.

In the ongoing history of visual representation of data, many unusual forms of graphs and diagrams have been developed. Some of the most striking graphs were devised by a statistician or scientist to represent a single, unusual data set in a new way. Even now, new standard forms are taking their place in the statistician's repertoire beside the more familiar bar graph or histogram.

So, while we do want students to use and interpret standard forms of graphs, we also want them to learn that, like other mathematicians and scientists, they can picture data in their own, individual ways. These pictures or diagrams or graphs are tools in the data analysis process. Through constructing their own representations, students can become more familiar with the data, understand the data better, begin to develop theories about the data, and, if they are going to "publish" their findings, communicate what they know about the data to an audience.

Shown on this page are some of the ways second and third graders have represented their findings from the sink and float experiment. None of these exactly follow a standard graph or table form, but all show the data clearly and effectively. ■

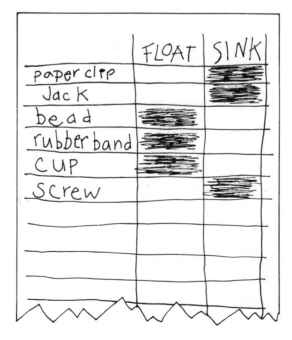

✎ TEACHER NOTE
Constructing your own categories

One key element in picturing categorical data is deciding on the categories themselves. Too often, data collection and representation in the primary classroom are tied to predetermined categories. That is, the categories are defined *before* the data are collected. In one classroom, for example, some students decided to do a survey about favorite foods. Anticipating the difficulties students would have in organizing the wide variety of answers they were likely to get, the teacher suggested that they limit their survey to five predetermined choices. The students chose five foods—pizza, ice cream, peanut butter, potato chips, and spaghetti. While this step certainly simplified their task, it also obscured the richness and diversity they might have seen in their results. Unfortunately, the students also lost some of their initial enthusiasm at this point in the process; this more limited survey was much less interesting to them than their original idea.

The sink-and-float experiment demonstrates that important categories may not be known ahead of time, before data collection and analysis. As students experiment and learn more about their data, some realize that SINK and FLOAT alone do not adequately describe all the phenomena they are encountering.

Here is a part of a discussion in one small group:

MAYA: The paper disintegrated. It was crumpled up and it broke up into little pieces.

GLENN: The paper drowned.

CHRISTINA: The nail drowned and the pipe cleaner sinks . . .

GLENN: But the plastic stick is halfway, the stick part goes down and the top stays up.

MAYA: But it never goes all the way down, it's not like the nail.

CHRISTINA: And the paper cup, it sinks and floats and gets softer.

[*Coming by the group as she circulates, the teacher hears the last remark.*]

How could it sink and float?

CHRISTINA: First it floats, then it sinks when the water goes in, and it sinks and gets softer.

MAYA: But you can make it just float if you put it down so the water doesn't go in.

GLENN: If things *sink*, we're going to put a column with S, and one with F for *floats*.

MAYA: And we need one for sink *and* float, S *and* F.

CHRISTINA: But don't count the things that float and get soft and sink. If it gets soft and sinks—we need a whole new column for that.

This group actually ended up with five columns: (1) *sink*, (2) *float*, (3) *sink and float*, (4) *floated, got soft, sunk*, and (5) *sunk, got soft*. Other groups invent their own versions of these and other categories: *sinks quickly, sinks slowly, sinks then floats, sometimes sinks, sometimes floats, floats if put down softly*.

Only through observing, recording, and thinking about the data can students construct truly meaningful categories that provide important information about their results. This process encourages even young children to begin to make their own observations and draw their own conclusions. They encounter an important idea about data analysis—that different observers may see the data in different ways, and that each observer has the chance to contribute a new and interesting idea through a different way of seeing and describing. ■

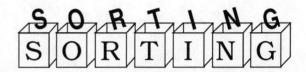

Sorting: Groups and Graphs

PART 3
Projects in data analysis

A note on the final projects

Part 3 of *Sorting: Groups and Graphs* includes two investigations.

The first investigation, *Animals in the neighborhood*, provides further experience in developing categories and sorting data. Note that the first session of the *Animals* investigation is part of the core activities of the unit. Optional Sessions 2 and 3 can be done to turn the investigation into a complete end-of-unit project, if you want to substitute a more extended *Animals* investigation for the suggested final project, *Investigating scary things*.

The second investigation, *Investigating scary things*, is the final project for the unit. In this investigation students collect data about what they are afraid of and compare their own data to information collected from adults about their fears when they were children. The *Scary things* investigation has

been used successfully by teachers in a variety of schools, including urban, suburban, and rural settings. Second and third graders are engaged by the topic, can draw on their own experiences, and are eager to collect data from others. Because students collect data from their parents, it also provides connections between home and school and opportunities for satisfying parent-child interactions.

Inevitably, any discussion of "scary things" taps into children's deepest feelings and concerns. It is critical that all students be able to participate freely and that none of their ideas be rejected as inappropriate for the classroom. If in your particular situation there are reasons that you prefer not to undertake this topic, we suggest that you use only the extended version of *Animals in the Neighborhood* (Sessions 1–3) as the final data analysis project. ■

ANIMALS IN THE NEIGHBORHOOD

INVESTIGATION OVERVIEW

What happens

In this investigation students brainstorm a list of animals living in their neighborhood. Small groups work to categorize the animals according to how they move (fly, swim, walk, hop, and so on) and to construct a group graph showing the neighborhood animals in those categories.

The second and third sessions are optional. In these sessions, each small group devises a new question about neighborhood animals, sorts the animals into categories to answer this question, and creates a presentation graph to show how they have sorted their data. Use these sessions if you want to extend this investigation because your students are interested in the topic, because it fits with your science curriculum, or because you intend to use this as a final project in place of *Investigating scary things*.

If you decide to use these optional sessions for the final project, read the Teacher Note, *Phases of data analysis: Learning from the process approach to writing* (page 75).

Session 1 requires one class session of 45–50 minutes. Sessions 2 and 3 (optional) require two class sessions of 45–50 minutes each.

What to plan ahead of time

▼ Provide stick-on notes (such as Post-it notes) or index cards, about 40 for each small group (Sessions 1 and 2).

▼ Provide markers, pens, or pencils for each small group (Session 1).

▼ If you plan to do Sessions 2 and 3, save each group's cards or notes with the animal names written on them for use in the later sessions.

▼ Provide materials for making presentation graphs, including a variety of kinds of paper, markers, crayons, colored pencils, stick-on dots, and so forth (Sessions 2 and 3).

Important mathematical ideas

Constructing categories to describe the data. Students construct their own categories to describe how animals in the neighborhood move. At first, students will probably start off with a few categories, such as *walk*, *fly*, and *swim*. But as they arrange and rearrange their data, they will see the need for changing, adding, or refining their categories to accommodate new aspects of the data that they have noticed.

Constructing and refining clear definitions. As students think carefully about the similarities and differences among the neighborhood animals, they will encounter difficulties, confusions, and outright disagreements about how to sort them. Through discussion, students sharpen their definition of each category and decide how each category differs from the others (see the Dialogue Box, *Does a spider walk?*). The students' earlier work on the importance of negative information in sorting takes on new relevance in this process of clarifying category definitions. That is, in order for a category to be meaningful, it must *include* some things and *exclude* others. ■

SESSION 1 ACTIVITIES

Considering the problem: What animals live in our neighborhood?

Remind the students that they have been working on ways of collecting and sorting information.

Today we'll be collecting data by thinking about what we already know about the animals that live in our neighborhood.

Suppose you went on a walk near your house or around the school. It could be today or it could be some other time of year. What animals have you ever seen that live in your neighborhood? Some animals are easy to see and some are hard to see. We'll have a minute of quiet while you close your eyes. Think carefully about all the places near your house or near the school or places where you play, and about any animal you have ever seen. Try to picture different places you go and what animals you've seen there.

After some thinking time, invite the students to name the animals they have thought of. List the animals on the board or on chart paper as students name them. They will be copying these names later, so make the words large and legible. Be sure to give students enough time to think carefully about different seasons of the year and animals that might be difficult to find or hard to see (worms, fleas). The students can

decide whether they want to include pets or just animals found in their natural habitat.

There may be some animals your students have seen whose names they don't know. Find some way to identify them—maybe other students know what they are called, or you can make up a name for them (silver bathtub bug, little yellow bird).

Be prepared for a fairly long list to emerge in about 10 minutes of brainstorming (see the Teacher Note, *Animals in the neighborhood*, page 63).

Considering the problem: How do these animals move?

Do you remember how you made categories to show the results of your sink-and-float experiments? When scientists study animals, they sort them into different groups to help them think about how different animals are related to each other—how they're alike and how they're different. Today we're going to think about our neighborhood animals and make up categories for how they move. Who can tell me something about how one of these animals moves around?

Keep this discussion brief; small groups will be exploring the question further. For this introductory discussion, students might take turns imitating one animal's movement while other students guess which animal it is.

Write on the board a few of the words that

come up in this discussion, for example: *walks, flies, crawls, swims, hops.*

Here are some of the words I heard you use. In your small groups, you are going to sort these animals into categories to show how they move. You can use some of these words, but you don't have to use all of them. You might think of your own categories that are different from these. Remember that in our sink-and-float experiment, different groups thought of different categories? Maya's group had a category called "sinks, then floats;" Glenn's group had categories called "sinks quickly" and "sinks slowly." Lynne's group had a category called "floats if put down softly." I expect that you'll think of different categories this time, too. Your group will decide together on your categories.

Recording and organizing data: Small group work on graphs

You'll need to have all the animals, so, in your groups, I want you to quickly copy the animals' names from the board onto these cards. You'll put one name on each card. If you all work together, it won't take too long to copy the names. When you have all the animals, then you can start putting them together and naming your categories for how they move.

Assign the students to small working groups of three or four. Each group needs index cards or stick-on notes and a large surface on which to work (a section of the chalkboard, a table, the floor).

In their groups, students will copy the names of the animals onto index cards or stick-on notes, decide on categories that describe how the animals move, and create a graph or picture that shows which animals fit into each category. While copying the names may seem like a large task, second graders have been able to handle it quickly when all the group members work on it.

As you move about the classroom, encourage students to arrange and rearrange their animals into groups. Some students will prefer to find animals that "go together" first and to decide what to name the categories only after they have grouped their animals. Other students may start out with certain categories in mind. Help these students to be flexible in finding new categories and modifying or changing their old categories if some animals do not fit their initial scheme.

Ask students to be as clear as they can about the definitions for their categories, but expect them to classify the animals in ways that adults might not. Encourage students to sort the animals in whatever ways make sense to them, and to articulate why they are putting certain animals into certain categories. It's important that the students discuss their reasoning with one another as much as they can. Students may not always agree, but should be encouraged to resolve

differences by clarifying the definitions of their categories (see the Dialogue Box, *Does a spider walk?*, page 62).

The discussion of categories might be very animated. At this point in the unit, many students should be able to sustain their own small-group discussions.

As students make their decisions, they group the index cards or stick-on notes in bar graphs, clusters, or whatever arrangement they think of (see the Teacher Note, *Animals in the neighborhood*, page 63). These graphs need not be permanent. If the students are using stick-on notes, they can move the notes to a large piece of paper once they are satisfied with their arrangement.

If you plan to extend this investigation, save the index cards or notes for use in the next session.

Summary (optional)

You may want to have students spend time looking at each others' graphs or have a brief whole-class discussion in which the groups report what categories they chose and why. Possible questions to discuss are: Do most of the animals in our neighborhood fly, walk, crawl? Are there any categories in which we have no animals or very few? Why is that? However, if good discussions have taken place during the small-group work, additional discussion at this point is not necessary. ■

66,99DIALOGUE BOX
Does a spider walk?

SAM: I've got one for FLIES.

CARLOS: What are you going to put in it?

SAM: Grasshopper.

CARLOS: It doesn't fly though.

JESSICA: It doesn't crawl and it doesn't walk.

CARLOS: It can walk.

ROSA: It hops.

CARLOS: No, it jumps.

SAM: Yeah, jumps.

CARLOS: Put jump. Let's make a card for JUMP.

ROSA: And rabbit goes in JUMP, too, and frog.

JESSICA: What about spider?

CARLOS: It walks. It has legs.

SAM: No, WALK isn't right. It's not like a dog or something. It can go up the walls and upside down on the ceiling. It climbs.

ROSA: Let's make one for CLIMBS.

SAM: Then I think raccoon goes there, too. It climbs up trees.

JESSICA [*starting to move other cards into CLIMBS*]: Squirrels can go up trees, and cats can, too.

CARLOS: But you're taking everything out of WALKS. This is too complicated. I don't think we should put CLIMB.

[*The teacher stops in, overhearing the last exchange.*]

You don't think you should use CLIMB?

CARLOS: No, Jessica's taking everything out of WALKS.

JESSICA: I am not.

What started you thinking about CLIMB as a category?

SAM: The spider, because it can go on the ceiling.

Uh-huh. So that wasn't the same as an animal that walks?

SAM: Yeah, cause, like, I walk, but I can't go upside down.

And what did you think, Carlos?

CARLOS: Well, then Jessica was going to put squirrel and cat and everything, but a cat doesn't climb all the time.

So you think a spider and a cat are really different in the way they get around?

CARLOS: Yeah.

What do the rest of you think about that? Are a spider and a cat the same or different?

ROSA: Well, I guess they're different. I mean they kind of both walk, but a spider sticks on with its feet.

Can anything else you have here do that?

JESSICA: Um . . . well, a fly can. It can crawl around anywhere.

SAM: Yeah, and a cockroach.

CARLOS: Yuck.

Well, it seems to me you have an important idea here. You're really thinking about the differences between things that can walk only on the floor or the ground and things that can walk anywhere.

[*The teacher moves on to another group.*]

ROSA: So let's put CLIMBS, but we'll just put things that can go anywhere, so squirrels and cats stay in WALK.

CARLOS: OK.

☛ In this discussion, the teacher intervenes to help students articulate and clarify the ideas that are emerging. Once she helps the students think a little harder about the differences between "walking" and "climbing," she points out that they are doing interesting thinking ("you have an important idea here"), but does not resolve the discussion for them. ■

✎ TEACHER NOTE
Animals in the neighborhood

Let students experiment with different arrangements for their categories. Here is a partial list of animals generated by a second grade class in an urban school (including pets):

dog	little bird	grasshopper
cardinal	bee	crow
mosquito	rat	ladybug
butterfly	worm	squirrel
mouse	raccoon	frog
turtle	blue jay	cockroach
cat	spider	ant
fly	rabbit	pigeon

Students set up a variety of categories and arrangements, such as those shown here.

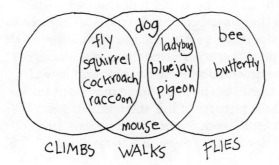

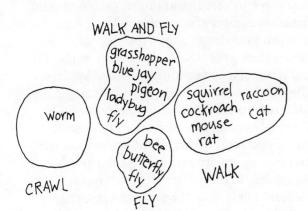

SESSION 2 AND 3 ACTIVITIES (OPTIONAL)

Considering the problem: How else could we sort the neighborhood animals?

Today, you're going to work in your small groups again to show something about the neighborhood animals, but this time your group is going to decide on what to show. Last time we sorted the animals to answer the question, "How do these animals move?" But there are many other questions we could ask about these animals. Can you think of other questions?

Accept ideas from students for 5–10 minutes. You may need to start off the discussion with a few sample questions, such as: Where do the animals live? What do they eat? How big are they? Are they fierce or gentle? What kinds of sounds do they make? In which seasons of the year can we find them? Which animals are domesticated, which are wild?

Organizing the data: Constructing new categories

Students work in their small groups. They first decide on what question they will ask, then use their index cards or stick-ons (saved from the previous session) to arrange and rearrange their data as they decide on categories. Note that students could look at an attribute such as size, even if they do not know exact measurements, by defining categories such as SMALL, MEDIUM, and BIG, or SMALLER THAN A MOUSE, AS BIG AS A MOUSE, and BIGGER THAN A MOUSE. Students may not want to include all the animals from the previous session's list, or they may want to add new animals.

Collecting more data: Using resources (optional)

During this process, questions are bound to arise. Students will find they are not sure or disagree about how to classify some of the animals. Tell each group to record their unanswered questions, for example: Are raccoons fierce or gentle? Is a mouse bigger or smaller than 6 inches? What does a crow eat? Can a squirrel sometimes be a pet? Help students do their own research to find answers to these questions through one or more of the following:

▼ Take a class trip to the school or public library so that students can look at the available books about animals.

▼ Set up a library corner in the classroom with books and magazines that have information about local animals. (*Ranger Rick*, a monthly magazine for children published by the National Wildlife Federation, is one good source).

▼ Invite a speaker from a local science museum, wildlife refuge, or branch of the Audubon society to answer students'

questions about local animals. Such a speaker may also be able to provide information on other animals that live in the vicinity but are not often seen.

Organizing the data: Making a presentation graph

Once the students have developed their categories and have sorted the data, each group will jointly make a more permanent presentation graph that shows their question, their categories, and how they have sorted the animals into the categories. Some groups might simply paste the index cards or stick-ons they have been using onto a large piece of paper; others may want to draw their graph rather than using the cards. Encourage students to decide on their own way of representing the data. Some may want to include pictures of the animals. Students can begin work on the graph in Session 2 and devote all of Session 3 to finishing it.

Extension: Collecting more data

If possible, take a class walk around the neighborhood and record all the animals that you see. This is a good opportunity for students to practice being careful observers. You might assign pairs of students to watch for particular kinds of animals; for example, some pairs might focus on animals that can be seen above our heads (birds, squirrels), other pairs on animals that can be seen on the ground (ants, dogs).

This activity could be done several times during the school year. Keep the graphs so that you can use them to compare animal populations in different seasons. What animals do you find in the fall, winter, spring? Are there more flying animals in the spring? Are there fewer animals that walk on the ground in the winter, or are they just harder to see? How many of each type of animal do you see during a week? Collecting and recording data about neighborhood animals can be integrated into a science curriculum that focuses on changing seasons, animal lives, or interdependent relationships in the environment.

Invite a grandparent who has lived in the local area since childhood to speak to the class. What changes have there been in animal life?

These activities can lead to new projects and new ways to sort the animals. Depending on the community, students may have little detailed knowledge about the animals that live in their area. One urban third grade, for example, decided to study types of spiders. They took walks to find spiders, brought spiders into the classroom (temporarily) for observation, drew pictures, wrote descriptions, and read books about spiders. In the process, many students (and their teacher) overcame their squeamish reaction to spiders! For data analysis activities, they sorted spiders according to which ones live outside and which inside, as well as by the types of webs they construct. ■

INVESTIGATING SCARY THINGS

INVESTIGATION OVERVIEW

What happens

This investigation provides a more extended problem in data analysis and classification on the topic of "scary things." After reading aloud books about scary things and discussing what children are afraid of, students draw pictures of their "most scary things" and try to group them into categories. The class develops a giant bar graph using the categories they have developed.

Finally, students carry out a survey of adults they know to find out what frightened them when they were children. They classify the adult data, make graphs or pictures of these results, and compare the adult data with their own.

The activities take five class sessions of 30–45 minutes each.

What to plan ahead of time

▼ Select one or two age-appropriate picture books about children's fears to read aloud to the class (Session 1). Possible titles include:
There's a Nightmare in My Closet, Mercer Mayer (Dial Books for Young Readers, 1968);
I Hear a Noise, Diane Goode (E. P. Dutton, 1988);
What's Under My Bed?, James Stevenson (Greenwillow Books, 1983).

▼ Provide large (5- by 8-inch) index cards (or substitute half a sheet of drawing paper). You will need at least one for each student and some extras for students who want to make more than one picture or who need to start again (Session 2).

▼ Have masking tape or thumbtacks handy for attaching students' cards to the chalkboard or bulletin board (Session 2). Also suitable for this purpose is a glue stick with a removable adhesive (such as Dennison's Tack-a-Note), which lets you fasten pieces of paper temporarily to the chalkboard, converting them to removable notes.

▼ Duplicate Student Sheet 1 (page 79), a survey sheet that students can use for collecting data from adults (optional, Session 2).

▼ Students will need time to collect data from their parents or other adults between Sessions 2 and 3.

▼ After students have collected their survey data, prepare a set of index cards listing the adult fears, one per card, for each small group (Session 4). Alternatively, write the adult fears on a sheet that can be cut apart and provide scissors. (Students need to have each adult "scary thing" written on a single card or piece of paper that can be moved around for grouping purposes.)

▼ Provide materials for making presentation pictures and graphs, including large plain and squared paper, crayons or markers, index cards (Sessions 4 and 5). Second and third graders enjoy making large pictures or graphs on chart paper (see the Teacher Note, *Is it a picture or a graph?*, page 76). If possible, provide a variety of sizes, from 11- by 17-inch drawing paper to 27- by 32-inch chart paper, both plain and squared.

Important mathematical ideas

Collecting and recording survey data. For the first time in this unit, students will be collecting and recording data outside the classroom. Spend some time helping students plan how they will ask their question. Emphasize the importance of writing down people's answers accurately.

Constructing your own categories to describe the data. Students determine their own categories to describe how their own and, later, the adults' "scary things" can be grouped. In this investigation, the categories help them organize the two sets of data so that they can make some comparisons. As in the sink-and-float experiment, students will

find that there are different ways to look at a set of data which lead to different approaches to classifying the data.

Comparing two data sets. Throughout this unit, students have been looking carefully at similarities and differences. In this final investigation, the process is expanded as students compare one whole set of data (students' own "scary things") to another set of data (what adults thought were "scary things" when they were children). Support students in making general statements about the two sets of data and ask them to interpret what they notice: What is the same? What is different? Why might this be true?

Experiencing all the phases of the data analysis process. A sustained investigation like this one is somewhat different from the shorter-term investigations done earlier in this unit. Here students have time to collect, think about, categorize, display, compare, and interpret data. See the Teacher Note, *Phases of data analysis: Learning from the process approach to writing*, for a description of more extended investigations.

Making presentation graphs and reporting on data analysis activities. This is a chance for your students to review what they have done in the investigation and to write about their process and their findings. Many students find writing about a mathematical experience to be very challenging and satisfying. Writing about mathematics needs to be encouraged, since it provides both an

avenue for creative expression and a way to express mathematical concepts in "plain language." Some students find it easy to write about their presentation graphs; others find it difficult. The reports or summaries can be fairly short, but should contain thoughtful treatment of both the mathematical content and the interpretation of their data. ■

SESSION 1 ACTIVITIES

Considering the problem: Introduction and reading aloud

We are going to be doing a study about things people are scared of—what children are scared of, and what adults were scared of when they were children. To help you start thinking about scary things, I am going to read a book about one child's idea of what's scary.

Read aloud one or two picture books about children's fears. Since the pictures are important, be sure to show them as you read.

Considering the problem: What are children scared of?

Ask students to talk about what things they or other children they know are scared of. To make this discussion a little less personal, some good discussion starters are: *What were you scared of when you were little? What are children your age scared of? What are people you know scared of?* By putting the questions this way, students do not have to admit that they are scared of anything! No matter how you phrase the question, students are likely to bring in lots of stories about themselves, their friends, or people in their family (see the Dialogue Box, *What are you scared of?*, page 67). In this first session, allow students time to recount examples and tell stories, but keep the discussion moving

so that it doesn't get stuck on a single topic, such as a particular scary movie.

Of course, this discussion must be handled sensitively, since there are very real, as well as imaginary, things that children may be afraid of. However, children often think that they're the only ones who are afraid of things, so this discussion can in fact be a comforting one (see the Teacher Note, *Starting to talk about scary things*, page 68).

Extension: Reading about others' fears

If you or your students have access to a school or public library, visit the library to find other books about being afraid. ■

❝❞DIALOGUE BOX
What are you scared of?

Now that we've talked about the books we read this morning, let's talk about the kinds of things that *you* think are scary. You can either tell us what scares you or what things scare people you know.

KATIE: When I watch a scary movie, when it's over I have a dream of it.

Movies sometimes scare you.

CHRISTINA: Sometimes after I watch something scary, when I go to sleep, I dream about them and I make them worse.

ALAN: One day I went to bed and I heard this noise but I found out it was my mother in the kitchen.

SEAN: Since I don't get tired, I stay up late. I hear noises and then cars go by with their lights on. I think there are robbers in the house. Then I have a dream that they will come in and take my sister.

I know what you mean. When I was in second grade, when my sister and I were alone, we'd hear the house creak. We'd walk around with a flashlight and a hammer in case a monster might get us.

[*Laughter.*]

PAUL: Wind in the night.

(Dialogue Box continued)

LYNNE: Sometimes the curtains blow in and that scares me.

KIMARA: Sometimes I get really scared when someone comes in the room, and I'm reading and I don't hear them, and I get scared.

BILLY: Yeah, once my father was watching TV and I came in and touched him and he jumped.

Because he was concentrating so hard?

SERENA: Sometimes when we eat dinner, the shutters bang in the kitchen and scare me.

MARK: Sometimes after a movie, I'm afraid to go to sleep because I might have nightmares.

So far, you've talked about movies, nightmares, scary noises, and being startled. A lot of you talked about things that happen at night or bedtime. Those are all things that are definitely scary! Now, can anyone think of some really different kinds of things that scare you or other people you know? It doesn't have to be just at night or bedtime.

LENA: My dad's afraid of dogs, that's why we can't have a dog. My mom told me that when he was little he got chased by a dog, and had to climb up a tree, and he was really scared, so then he got scared of dogs.

That's interesting. I wonder if there are other people who are scared of some kind of animal.

ALAN: Well, when I was little, I used to be afraid of bees . . . ■

✎ TEACHER NOTE
Starting to talk about scary things

Students will have a lot to say about this topic. The discussion is likely to wander in many different directions. Students will want to tell stories about their own scary experiences. Teachers have found that it is a good idea to let this discussion range widely and not to worry about focusing it during this first session.

Inevitably, students' real fears and concerns will emerge in this discussion. Teachers have used this investigation to provide support for students who have real fears; students find it reassuring to hear that they are not the only ones who are scared of something. Some teachers have been willing to volunteer information about their own fears. Even if a student does not verbalize a particular fear he or she has, simply having this topic be one that is allowed and encouraged in the classroom can help students overcome the isolation they can feel when they think that fears must be kept hidden and secret.

Manage the discussion so that it does not get stuck on one topic. For example, in one classroom, students talked a great deal about one or two particular horror videos. Eventually, in order to elicit some new ideas, the teacher needed to say, "It certainly sounds as if a lot of you are scared by these videos. Now, what about some very different kinds of things that can be scary?"

What might be considered "difficult topics" can arise in this discussion. Often a simple, matter-of-fact response can acknowledge and include a child's suggestion without raising complex issues that the group as a whole might not be ready for. For example, in one class a student suggested "rape people," to which the teacher responded, "You mean people who would hurt someone else. They are called rapists."

It is critical to accept as legitimate *all* the fears students raise. Comments such as "Oh, you don't need to be afraid of that, that's just make-believe," or "Of course, you know there's really nothing under your bed," appear to define some children's fears as less legitimate than others. Almost all of us have had a scary experience that seems silly in retrospect, but there's no denying that we certainly felt scared at the time. Acknowledge and accept students' stories matter-of-factly, communicating the idea that we're all afraid of things sometimes. ■

SESSION 2 ACTIVITIES

Collecting data: What are our most scary things?

Write on the chalkboard "Our Most Scary Things." Tell students that today you are going to make a giant graph to show their ideas about what is most scary for children their age.

Ask students to choose something that they think is scary and draw it on the index card or paper you provide. They can pick something from the first session's discussion or something else that they have thought of since. They do not need to put their names on the pictures. They should also write a word or short phrase describing the picture (this is important in case you can't tell what the picture shows). Give students 5 or 10 minutes to make their picture and words. It's best if they use crayons or markers so the pictures will show up when they are put together into a graph.

In this second session, students are often more willing than they were in Session 1 to share their real fears. Teachers have found that it's important to keep the pictures anonymous, so students feel freer to draw something meaningful to them. One teacher said to the students, "This is personal and special. You can draw or write what you are afraid of most on this card."

Collect all the cards. Use the board or chart paper to quickly jot down all the words or phrases that describe the pictures (see the Dialogue Box, *Some second graders' scary things*, page 70, for examples of students' scary things). Then read the list aloud, or have students read it aloud.

Organizing the data: Which scary things go together?

You've thought of a lot of scary things. Let's see if there are any that go together. Remember how you sorted your "thing collections" into groups of things that went together? Are there some of these scary things that could go into a group together?

Take students' suggestions for grouping things and write them on the board or chart paper. For example, categories might include MONSTERS, ANIMALS, SCARY PLACES, THE DARK, MEAN OLDER KIDS. Students will have to think about names for their categories, what fits in the categories, and how inclusive to make them. It is usually easier for students at this age to think *first* about which

scary things go together, *then* about what to call the category (see the Dialogue Box, *What goes with haunted houses?*, page 71).

As students come to agree on categories and which pictures fit in them, you can move the pictures into groups (using small pieces of tape on the chalkboard or tacks on the bulletin board) so that the students can see which pictures are classified and which are still left to sort.

Organizing the data: A giant bar graph

Using the students' pictures and the categories they have generated, make a giant bar graph by listing the categories across the bottom of a section of the chalkboard or a large piece of paper, then taping or tacking each card above the name of its category. If there are a few unresolved issues, have students decide what to do. There may be one or two pictures that do not fall easily into any category and end up alone. Display the graph in a place where it can be seen easily during the rest of the *Scary things* sessions.

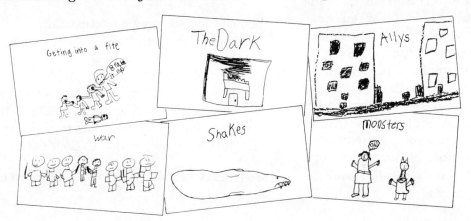

Our Scary Things

Monsters | Animals | Dark | Nightmares | Things that hurt the body | Dying

Considering the problem: What were adults scared of when they were little?

What do you think we would find out if we asked older people what they used to be scared of? Do you think your parents or teachers were scared about the same kinds of things when they were your age?

After some discussion, tell students that they will be carrying out their own survey to find out what adults were scared of when they were little. Agree on exactly what question they will be asking and write it on the chalkboard—for example, "What scared you the most when you were little?" Students can ask any adults they know—mothers, fathers, grandparents, or any adult friends. One way to organize this survey would be to make every child responsible, as homework, for asking the survey question to *two* adults.

Students may also want to ask some of their teachers; you might want to assign particular students to ask particular teachers. If you wish, duplicate and distribute Student Sheet 1 to give students an organized way to record their findings. Students can copy the survey question onto the top section of the sheet.

Extensions

Some students may be interested in collecting more data from students their own age. Each student could ask one or two other children after school, or you could arrange for some of your students to take a survey in another classroom. Add the new data to the giant bar graph. The new data may prompt students to change or add to their categories.

Some classes have been more interested in

what their parents are afraid of *now* than what frightened them when they were children. In some classes, the students and teacher have substituted or added this question to their study.

Integrate writing with this unit by having students write about scary experiences. ■

66 99DIALOGUE BOX
What goes with haunted houses?

CARLOS: I think mine about going into the basement and Amy's about going into the shed go together.

Why do you think those two go together?

CARLOS: Because they're both dark.

AMY: Yeah, and because they have spider webs.

ALAN: And there are lots of places things could hide.

Is there anything else on our list that could go with Amy's and Carlos's ideas?

KIMARA: Yeah, going into the back of my uncle's store at night.

Any others that go with these? . . . OK, what should we call this category?

JANE: DARK PLACES.

Is DARK PLACES OK?

BILLY: The one about walking through an alley at night is about dark places, too.

So should walking through an alley be in this category, or is it something different? What do you think?

ELISABETH: I think it's different, because the cellar and the shed are inside places, and the alley is outside.

So should one category be DARK INSIDE PLACES?

[*Later*] . . .

ROSA: Put strangers with murderers.

[*Murmurs of protest are heard from other students.*]

What do you think about that?

CHRISTINA: No, strangers don't have to be murderers. They could be really nice people, but you don't know that or maybe you see them coming at night so you think they're scary.

PAUL: Put strangers with haunted house.

Why?

PAUL: If you don't know anyone in the haunted houses, they might be strangers.

So if a stranger is in a haunted house, you'd be scared of them?

PAUL: Yes.

Someone else?

MAYA: I think strangers go with dark because it's like you don't know what's there in the dark and you don't know who the stranger is. That's why you're scared.

This is a hard one. There are a lot of different ideas about this. Let's think about strangers some more and come back to it later. Maybe getting more categories will help us decide where to put it, or maybe we'll decide it should be all by itself.

☞ Even though you may have clear ideas about how to categorize the scary things, try not to impose your categories on the students. It is important that they struggle on their own with what goes together and what to call the categories. For example, one class included ghosts, skeletons, rats, demons, goblins, bats, maggots, and Dracula in a category they called HAUNTED HOUSE— probably not the way adults would classify these diverse scary things! It is very likely that some things may fit in two categories or be hard to categorize. These are common and legitimate problems in classification. Remember that there are no absolute answers to these problems. What's important is that students think hard about the similarities and differences among the scary things and try to give good reasons for their ideas. ■

SESSION 3 ACTIVITIES

Considering the data: What did you find out from your parents?

Because students will probably be eager to share what they found out, begin with a brief general discussion.

What did you find out? Did you find some scary things that were the same as the things on our bar graph? Some things that were different?

Comparing adult and student data: A first look at similarities and differences

List all the scary things the students collected from adults on the board or on chart paper. Write clearly in large letters, as students will use this list later in the session.

Draw students' attention to the graph you made of their own scary things.

When we put our scary things on the graph, we figured out how we could put them together in groups, so we could describe what kinds of things second graders are scared of. The categories we came up with were [ANIMALS, HAUNTED HOUSES, THE DARK, THINGS THAT HURT THE BODY . . .]. Do you see any of the adults' scary things that would fit in these categories? Do you see any that don't fit? Do you think the same categories will work for the adult data?

Allow time for students to comment on the similarities and differences between their own data and the adult data. This discussion is a time for students to give their first impressions about the two sets of data and to start thinking about categories for the adult data (see the Dialogue Box, *Will the same categories work?*, following). Keep in mind that there will be an opportunity to continue this discussion at the end of Session 5 when the data have been organized into pictures and graphs.

Now is the time to prepare sets of index cards or cut-apart sheets listing all the different adult fears, for small-group use in Session 4. ■

66 99 DIALOGUE BOX
Will the same categories work?

DENNIS: My dad was afraid of dogs, so he could fit in ANIMALS.

MARK: And my aunt could too. Hers was spiders.

So we definitely have some scary things that fit in the ANIMALS category. Are there any others that you think fit in some of our categories?

JESSICA: Well, that one about, what Serena said about going up to a house on Halloween and the guy jumped out with a pumpkin. That could go in HAUNTED HOUSES.

TONY: And mine can, too, about my mom and the house with the vacant lot.

OK, so there's some other fears that are similar to ours. What else do you notice about things on the adult list? Anything that doesn't fit with our categories?

SAM: Being afraid of getting hit in school.

ROSA: Thunderstorms. We didn't have anybody afraid of thunderstorms.

JANE: That could go with DARK, though.

You think that thunderstorms could go in our DARK category? What do you think?

LENA: I don't agree, because what's scary about thunderstorms is the lightning and

(Dialogue Box continued)

the thunder, and our DARK things were like alleys and basements.

You think our DARK things were different? Do other people have opinions?

ALAN: Yeah, they're, like, places.

So you wouldn't put thunderstorms with DARK? Is there anything else on the adult list that might go with thunderstorms?

GLENN: Yeah, my mom's friend said he used to be afraid of the ocean.

You think that goes with thunderstorms?

GLENN: Yeah.

Can you explain how they go together?

GLENN: [*pause . . . shrugs*]

Well, maybe someone else can think of the words for it because I can see how ocean and thunderstorms might go together. Can anyone else add to Glenn's idea?

SEAN: Maybe because they're both wild and they can push you.

KATIE: The ocean can make big crashing sounds like thunder.

ELISABETH: And you get wet in the ocean and you get wet in a thunderstorm.

Those are interesting ideas. In your small groups, you'll have to make some decisions about which things you think go together.

EDDIE: I have another one that doesn't fit— Getting lost. Nobody in the class said getting lost . . . ■

SESSION 4 AND 5 ACTIVITIES

In these sessions, students organize the data they gathered from adults and then compare the adult data with their own class data. In Session 4, most groups will probably be able to decide on their categories, make their "rough draft" picture or graph, and begin work on their final presentation graph. Session 5 will be devoted to finishing the final graph and a class discussion about the students' findings. A few groups may need some extra time to finish their graphs or pictures. Make sure to leave 20–25 minutes for the final discussion so that your students can really think about comparisons between their own data and the adult data.

Small-group work: Organizing, classifying, and displaying the data

Today you're going to work in your small groups to figure out how to put the adult data into groups, just like we did for your own data about scary things. Later, after you have decided on your categories, you'll make a big picture or graph of all the adult scary things. Think hard about what goes together and what to call your categories. Just as when we did the sink-and-float experiment, different groups may come up with different ideas about what categories to use.

Form small working groups of three or four students. Give each group a set of adult-fears index cards or the cut-apart list you

prepared in advance. Also provide some blank index cards, pieces of paper, or stick-on notes on which they can write their categories. Each group should have a large flat surface (a table or the floor) on which to work, so they can spread out all the cards. (If they are working with a list, they will need to cut apart all the "adult scary things" before they start to work.)

I'm going to give each group a pack of cards that has all the adult scary things from the list we made yesterday. Each card names one of the things that you found out about in your survey. You can use the cards to decide which things go together.

The students' first task is to group the adult scary things until they are satisfied with their classification. The discussion about categories may be very animated. Encourage students to try out various categorization plans by moving the cards around to try different groupings and to change categories, add new categories, or discard categories as needed. When they decide on a category, they can write it on an index card or piece of paper in order to label that group of things.

As you move about the classroom, ask students for their reasoning—why do certain scary things fit in certain categories? Even if the students' reasons don't agree with what adults might say, it's important that the students discuss their reasoning with one another as much as they can, just as they did in the previous investigation, *Animals in the neighborhood.*

When students feel satisfied with their categories, it's time for them to start planning their final picture or graph. Encourage them to make their pictures or graphs both clear and interesting. People who look at the picture or graph should be able to understand clearly what it shows about the data they collected, but it can also use color or pictures to highlight important information and attract attention to its message (see the Teacher Note, *Is it a picture or a graph?*, page 76).

Post the final graphs where the rest of the students can easily see them.

Interpreting the data: Comparing "scary things" of adults and students

Ask students to think about their own data and the adult data: Which categories are the "most popular" for us? For our parents or teachers? Are there some categories that existed for our parents but not for us, or vice versa? Why might that be? Encourage students both to make simple comparisons ("We listed scary videos and our parents didn't") and to construct theories about why these observations might be true ("Maybe they weren't on when they were kids"). As part of this discussion, the different ways

different groups categorized the data will come up. Emphasize interesting differences, so that students are aware of alternative ways of sorting the data. Do different graphs show some different aspects of the adults' scary things?

Publishing findings: What did we learn from our "scary things" data?

Students can each write a few sentences to summarize what was most interesting about their findings, or you can put together a class story about the project by having students dictate to you what should be included. What did they find out about themselves? About adults? What was similar, what was different about what they said and what their parents said? What surprised them? What questions do they still have?

These reports can be posted along with the graphs and pictures to make a final Scary Things display. If students seem interested, they could present their research results to another class or to interested teachers.

Extension: Collecting more data

One class took a new all-class survey to end this unit. By this point, students had grown fairly comfortable with talking about scary things and were more willing to admit to their fears. Using the categories they had defined for their own scary things, they took a poll to see how many in the class were afraid of things in that category. The teacher

went through the categories, one by one.

Anyone who is afraid of anything in the ANIMAL category stand up . . . Anyone who is afraid of anything in the MONSTER category stand up . . .

Students could stand up for more than one category. Each time, a student counted how many were in the category, and the teacher quickly made a graph on the chalkboard. Students were fascinated with how many people were in each category. Their final graph looked like this:

Night-mares	Mon-sters	Animals	Dark places	Dying	Things that hurt
				17	
				X	
				X	
14				X	
X		13		X	13
X		X		X	X
X		X		X	X
X		X	10	X	X
X	9	X	X	X	X
X	X	X	X	X	X
X	X	X	X	X	X
X	X	X	X	X	X
X	X	X	X	X	X
X	X	X	X	X	X
X	X	X	X	X	X
X	X	X	X	X	X
X	X	X	X	X	X

✎ TEACHER NOTE
Phases of data analysis: Learning from the process approach to writing

The process of data analysis is similar to many other creative processes. Students doing data analysis follow the same processes that adults do; the analyses may be less complex, but the procedures are the same. In data analysis, as in writing or art, teachers help children do real work rather than stilted school assignments requiring fill-in-the-blank responses. The teacher's role is relatively subtle—shaping the process, asking questions that guide the students' progress toward their goals, hearing and responding to their ideas and theories. Students are expected to have something original and interesting to say, and the teacher provides an environment that enriches and supports students' self-expression.

Data analysis has many similarities to the process approach to writing, which typically includes four phases. The process starts with a *planning phase* (often called pre-writing or brainstorming). This is followed by the *writing phase*, when a very rough draft of ideas is first put down on paper. The third phase is the *revision* or *rewriting phase* when the writer elaborates, clarifies, restructures, and edits the piece. The final phase is the *publication phase*, when the writer's completed piece is shared with others. These processes may be reiterated until the piece of writing is finished.

Data analysis has four phases parallel to those in the writing process:

Phase One: Brainstorming and planning. During this time, students discuss, debate, and think about their research question. In some cases, defining and agreeing upon the question may take a considerable amount of time. Having defined the question and agreed upon terms, students consider possible sources of data, ways of recording them, and how they might organize themselves to collect needed information.

Phase Two: Putting it on paper. For the collection and representation of data, students develop their discovery drafts—what we call "sketch graphs"—the first draft of the information on which they base their developing theories. Students represent the data in a variety of ways to help them describe the important features. They use their first drafts as tools as they look for relationships and patterns in the data.

Phase Three: Revision. Writers are encouraged to share their drafts with their peers in order to determine how an audience perceives their work. Similarly, in the data analysis process, the students often present their sketch graphs, preliminary findings, and beginning theories to their working group in order to see whether their interpretations seem supported by the data, and whether others see things they haven't noticed.

Revision in data analysis may include finding new ways to organize and represent the data, developing better descriptions of the data, collecting additional data, or refining the research questions and collecting a different kind of data.

Phase Four: Publication or display. The nature of "publishing" the results of data analysis varies, just as it does for a story or essay. Sometimes students develop a theory that is the basis for a report on a particular topic; at other times they may develop a theory that inspires further investigation. A completed report of a data analysis investigation may involve a written description of the study with conclusions and recommendations, final presentation graphs of information previously displayed in working graphs, or a verbal or written presentation of the report to an interested audience.

When teachers think about the writing process, their role as facilitator and helper seems familiar and obvious. Of course students need time to think and revise their work! Of course they need to be challenged and led, sensitively, to the next level of awareness. The writing process seems more familiar to most of us than the mathematics process because we, too, have done writing.

The process of data analysis needs the same kind of teacher support. Students need to try their ideas, to rough them out, to be challenged and encouraged to go further in their thinking. It is important that they have time to think and to consider options—and vitally

important that they see their work as part of a process. Data analysis, like writing, is not cut and dried. There are many ways to approach a question and many conclusions to be drawn. Like writing, mathematical investigation is a creative blend of precision and imagination. ■

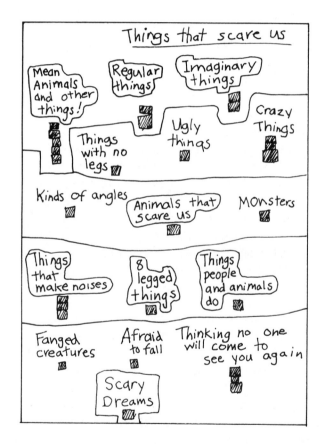

What interests second and third graders is the particulars of the data. They are intrigued that Rosa's dad was afraid of spiders, or that Alan's aunt used to think there was a monster under the bed when she was in second grade. In their representations, 7- and 8-year-olds often want to retain the individuality of each piece of data. They enjoy identifying individual names on their graphs or portraying the characteristics of their data through pictures.

Unlike upper elementary grade students, second and third graders are not quite ready to pull their attention away from individuals in order to summarize or describe a whole group. This interest in the individual and the particular leads to representations that are some mixture of picture, story, graph, and chart. Some students tend to use words and lists. Others tend to use a pictorial approach.

When given encouragement to represent the data in their own way, students at this age can create beautiful and effective representations. Some actual samples designed by second graders are pictured on page 74, on this page, and on the following page. Unfortunately, these samples do not show their creative and communicative use of color, both for the pictures and to set apart the different categories.

Students' picture-graphs will not necessarily follow the conventions of graph-making that we would expect upper elementary grade students to use. Their pictures may not be all the same size or categories may not be lined up so that the number of things in each category can be compared directly. However, when students adopt the conventions of what they think graphs are "supposed" to look like, they often produce rather mundane bar graphs which actually do not communicate much information.

Therefore, encourage students to use their creativity and inventiveness in making their presentation graphs, so that someone who looked at the graph would be as intrigued as they are by the data. ■

Things That Scare Our Relatives			
mean animals and other things	✓✓✓✓	kinds of angles	✓
regular things	✓✓	crazy things	✓✓✓
Things with no legs	✓✓	ugly things	✓
Imaginary things	✓✓	monsters	✓
things people and animals do	✓	scary dreams	✓
eight legged things	✓	fanged creatures	✓
thinking no one will come to see you again	✓✓✓	afraid to fall	✓
things that make noises	✓✓✓		

Things that scare adults when they were little

Animals with and without legs | People Who Are Alone | Noises | Monsters | Things That People and Animals Do | Imaginary Things | Animals With Four Legs | Things That Have water | Scary People | High Places | Empty Places | Dark Places

SCARY THINGS SURVEY

Our survey question: _____

_____

_____

Answers from people I asked:

1. _____

_____

_____

2. _____

_____

3. _____

_____

4. _____

_____

_____

KRYPTONITE

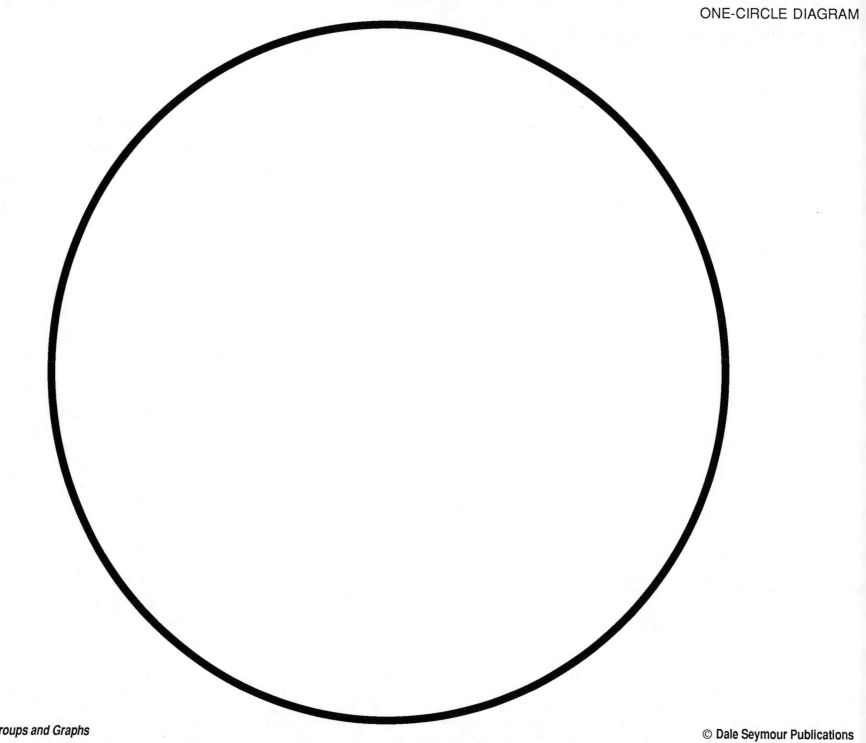

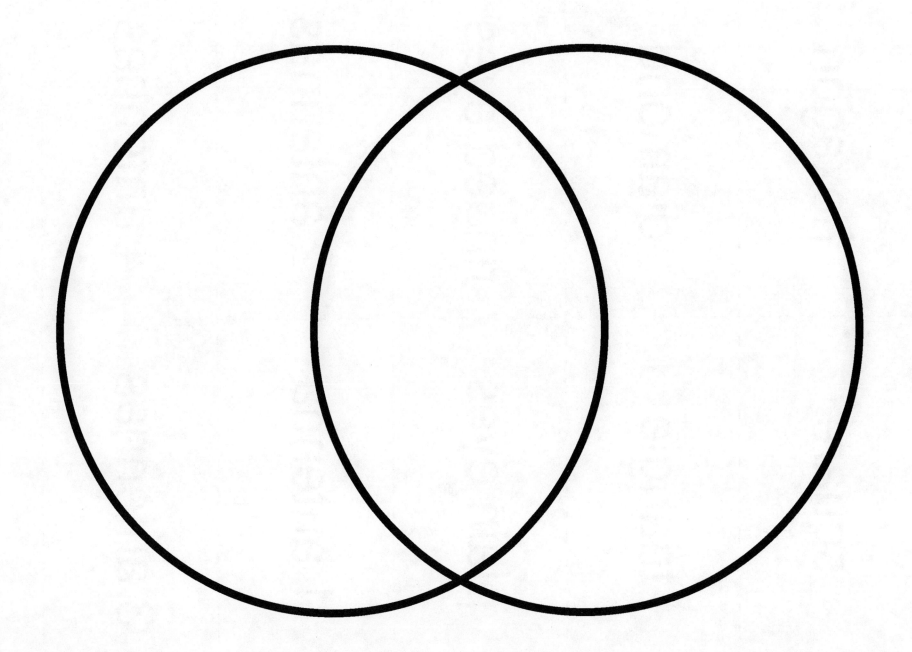

hexagon

diamond

ringed eyes

2 antennas

4 antennas

square

triangle

plain eyes

1 antenna

3 antennas

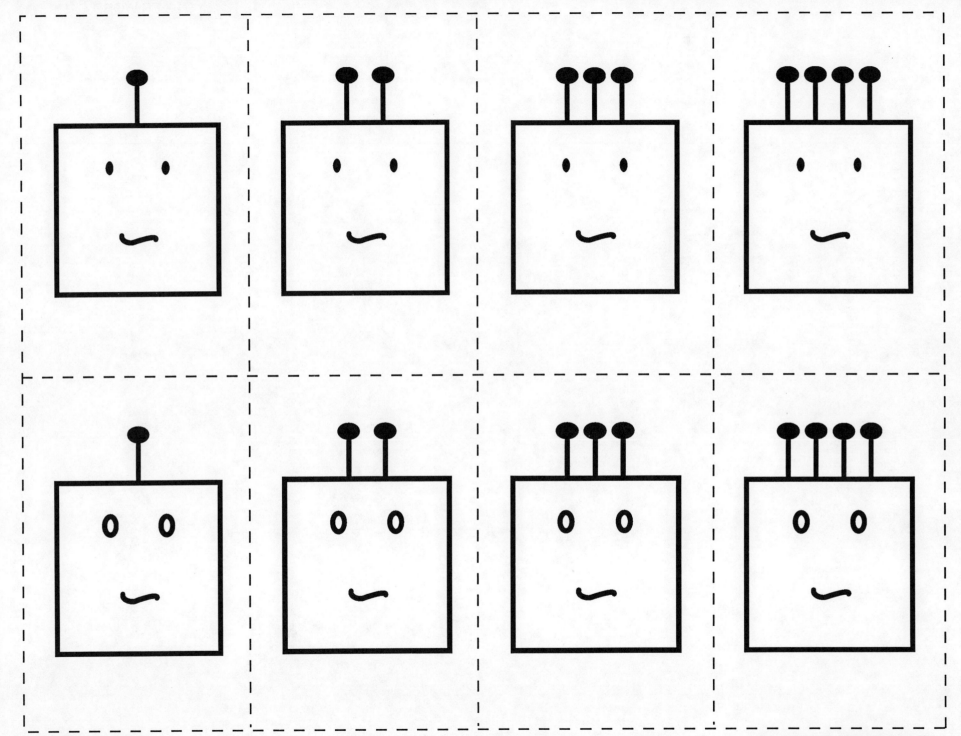

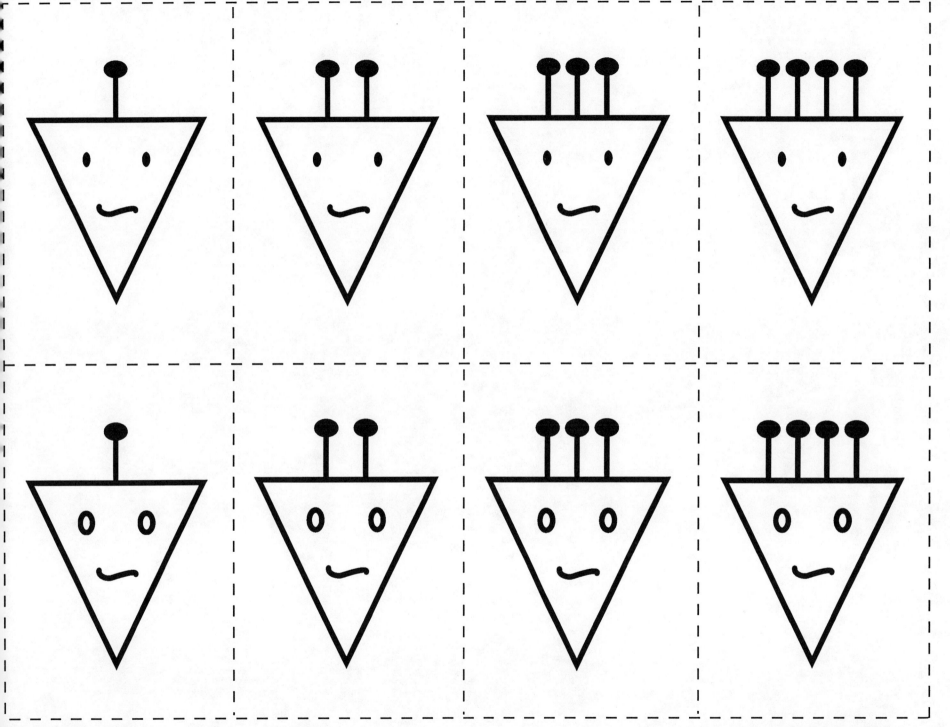

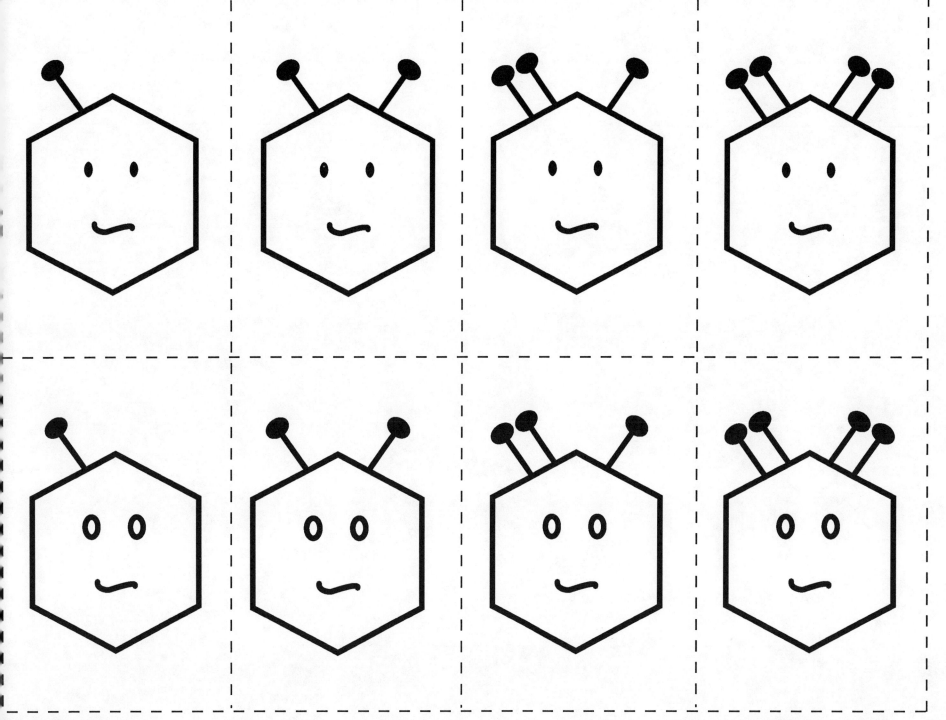

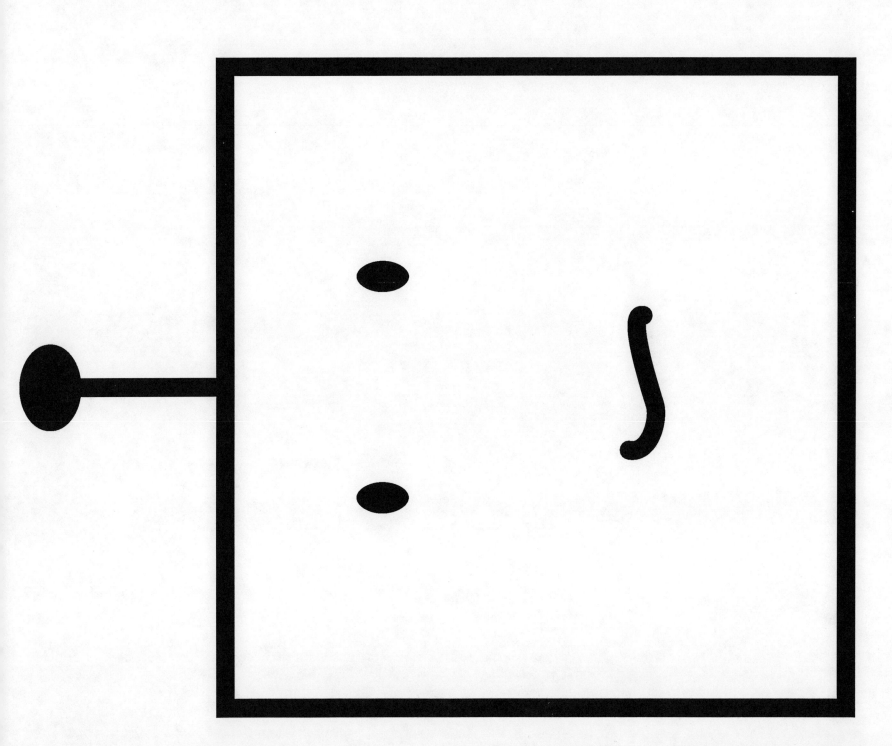

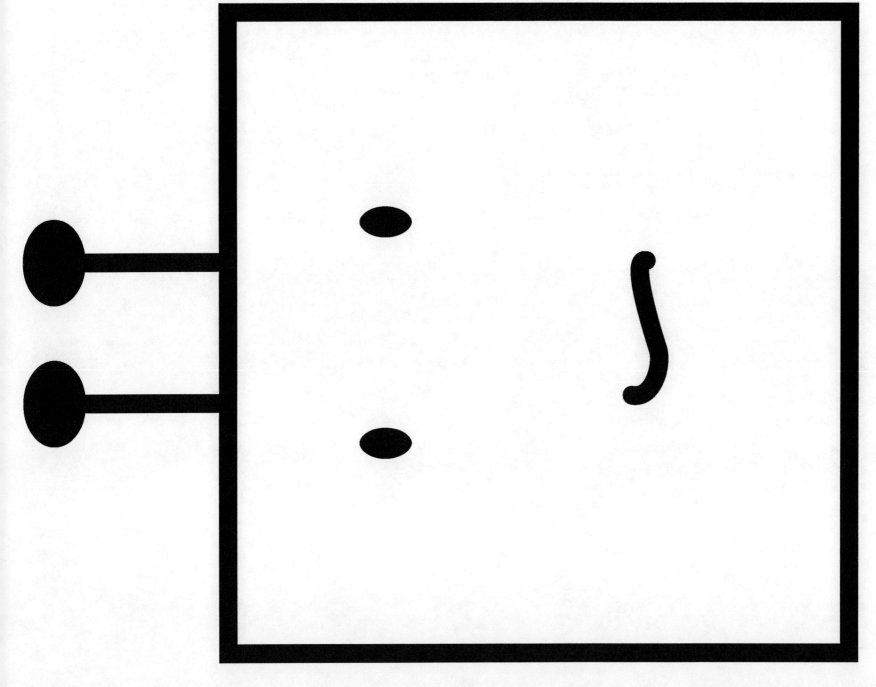

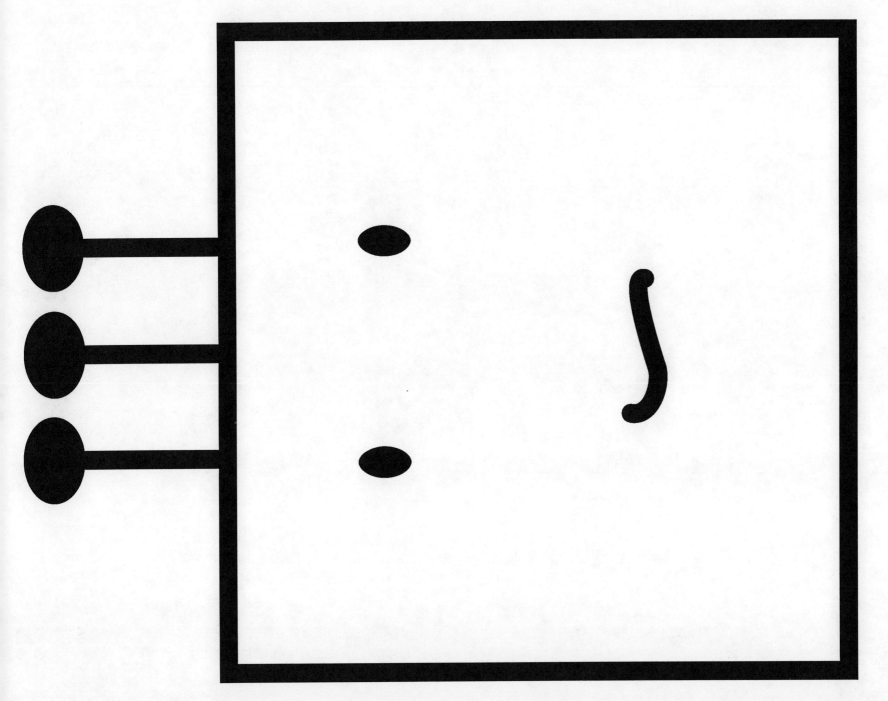

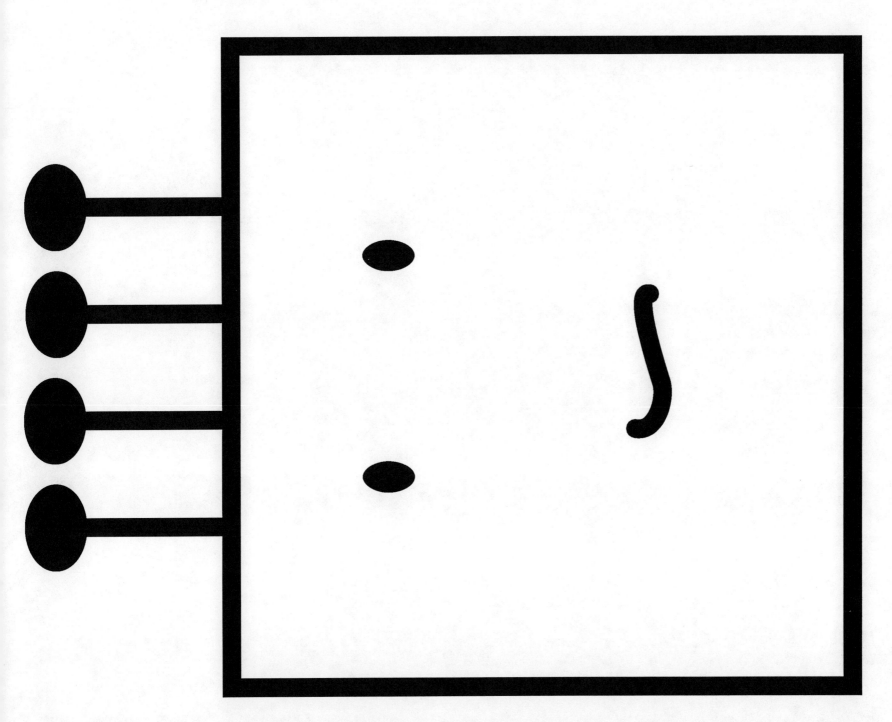

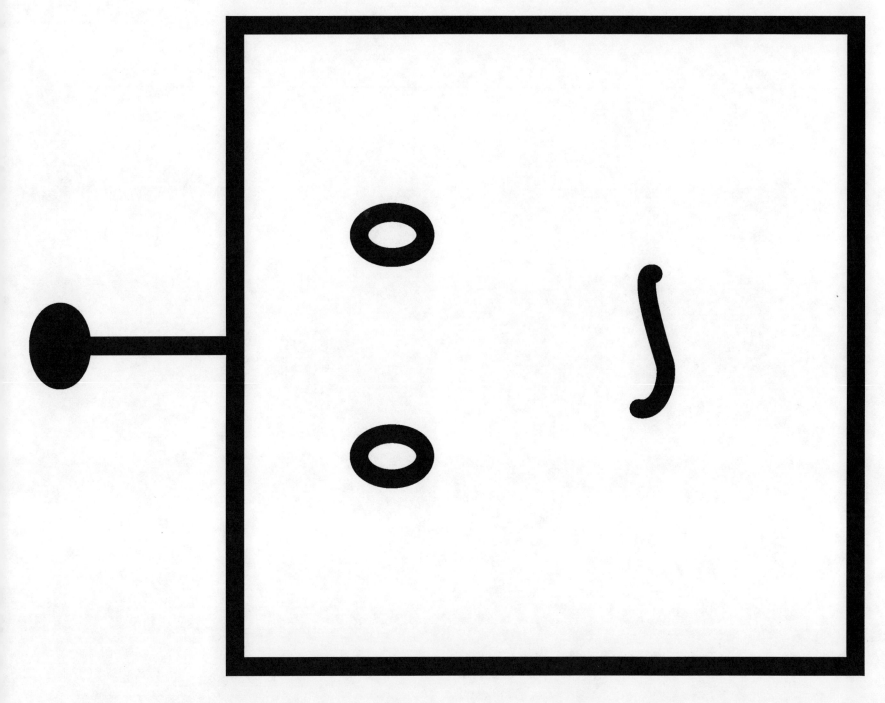

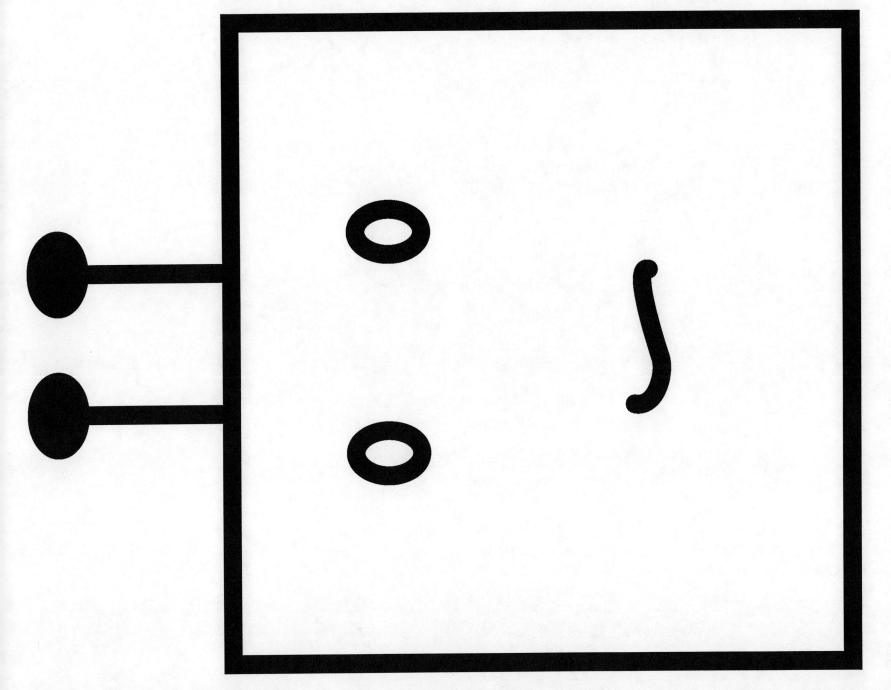

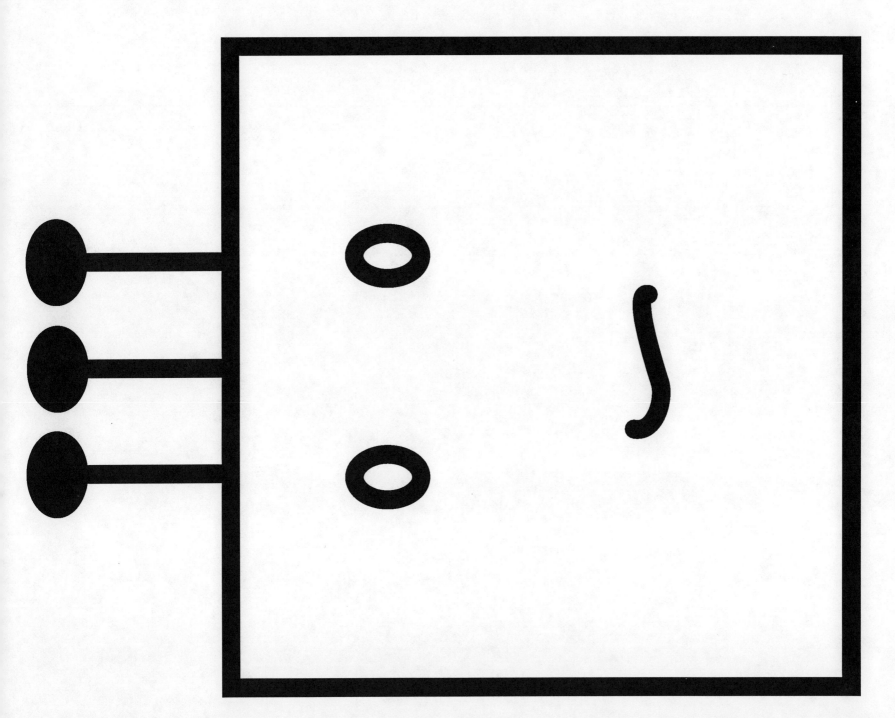

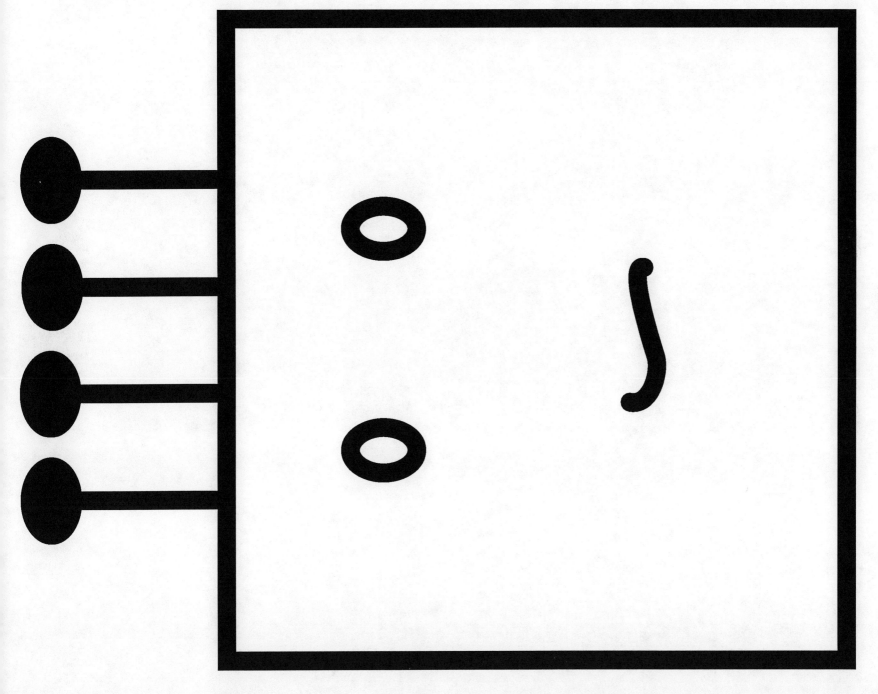

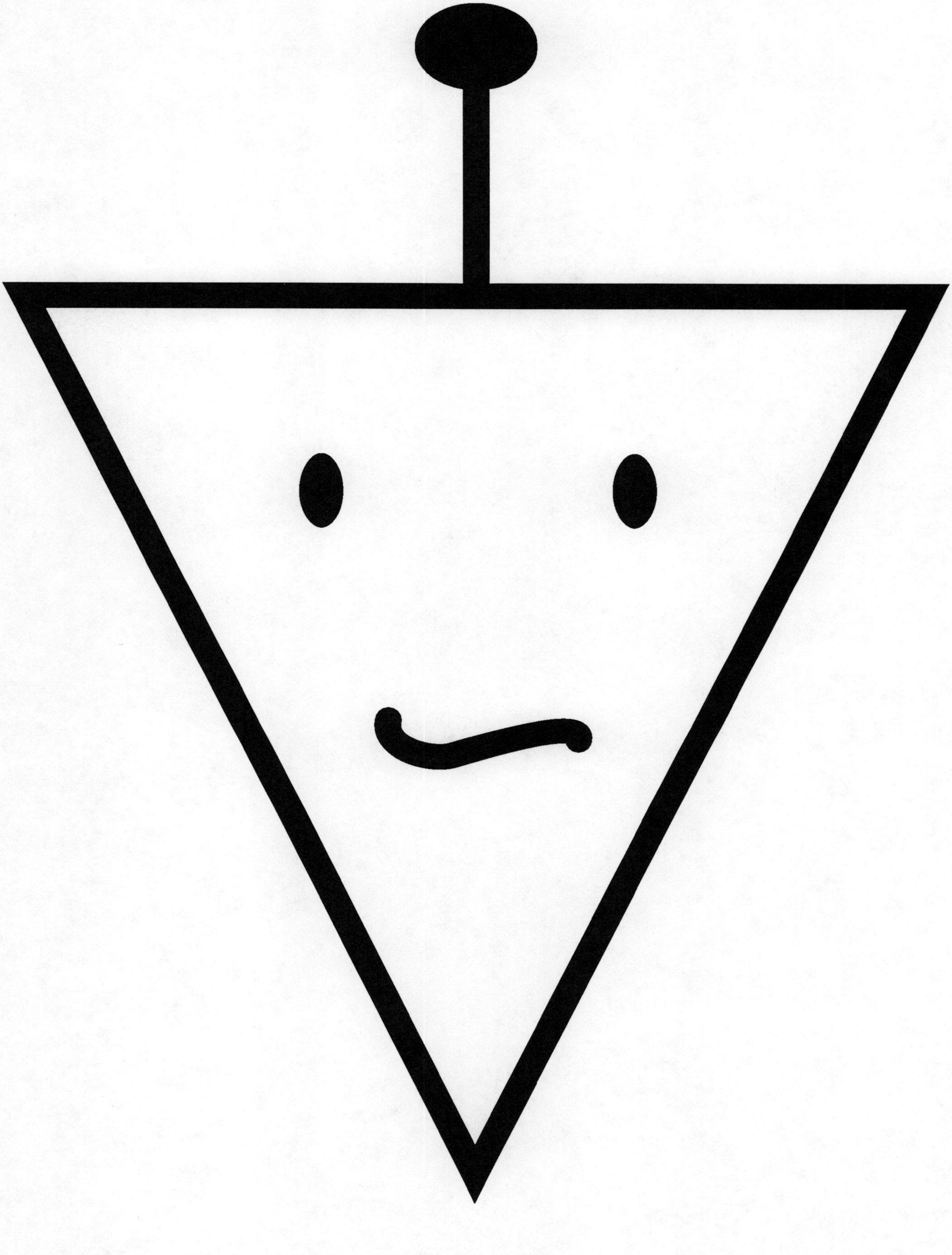

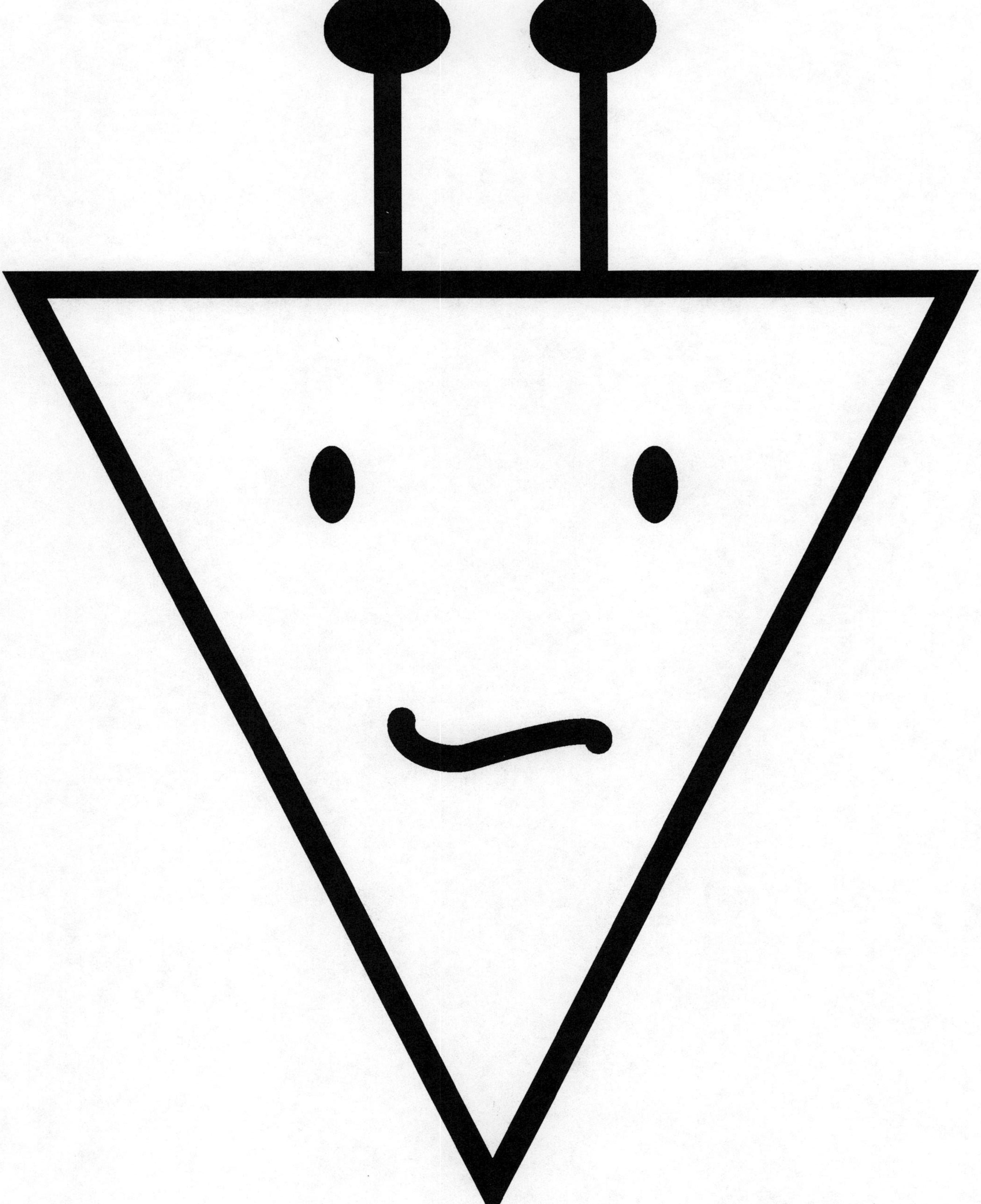

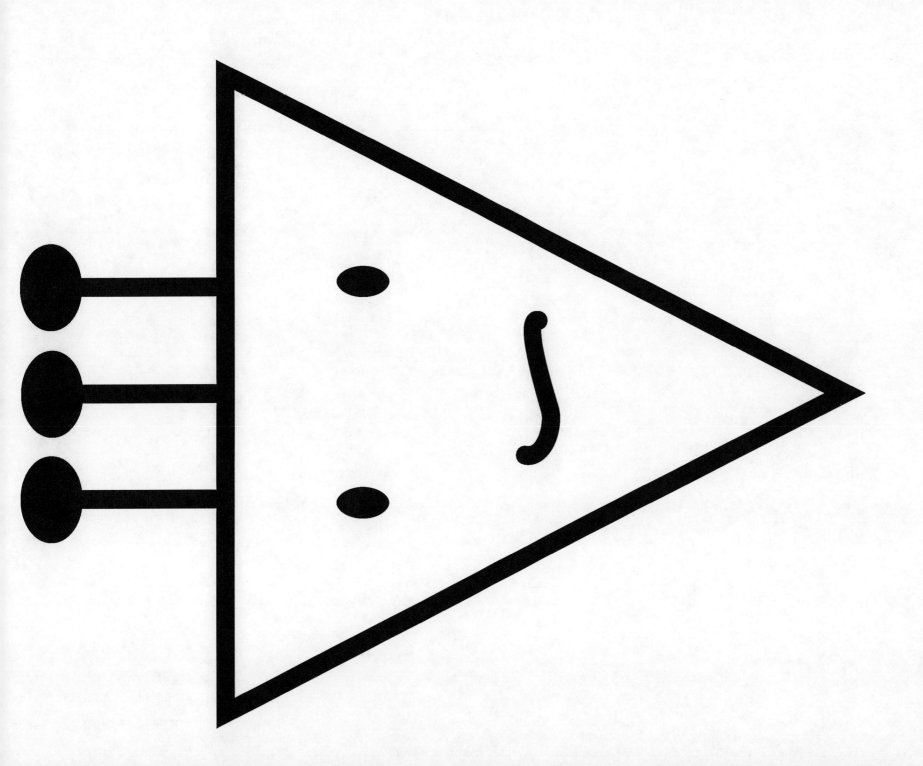

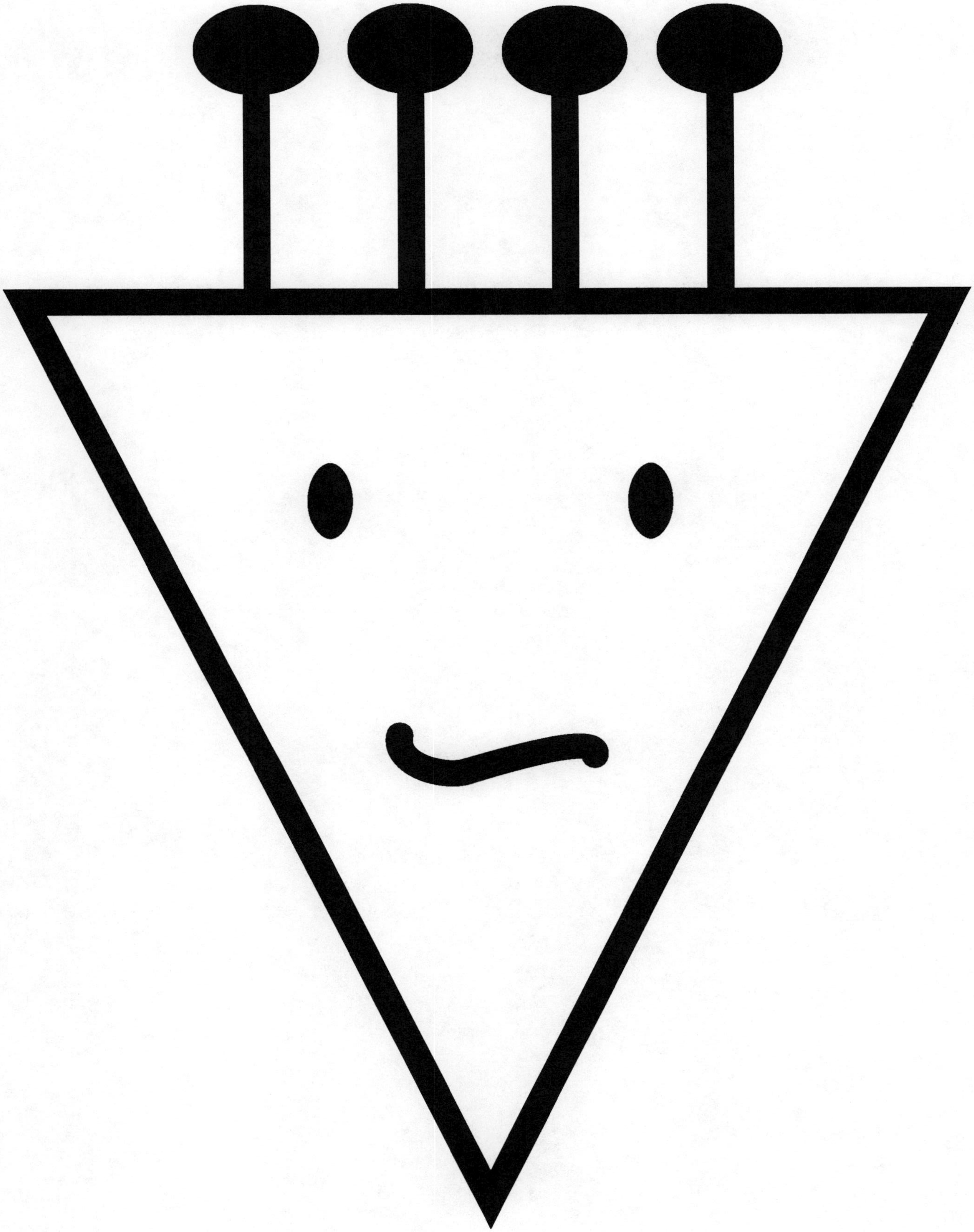

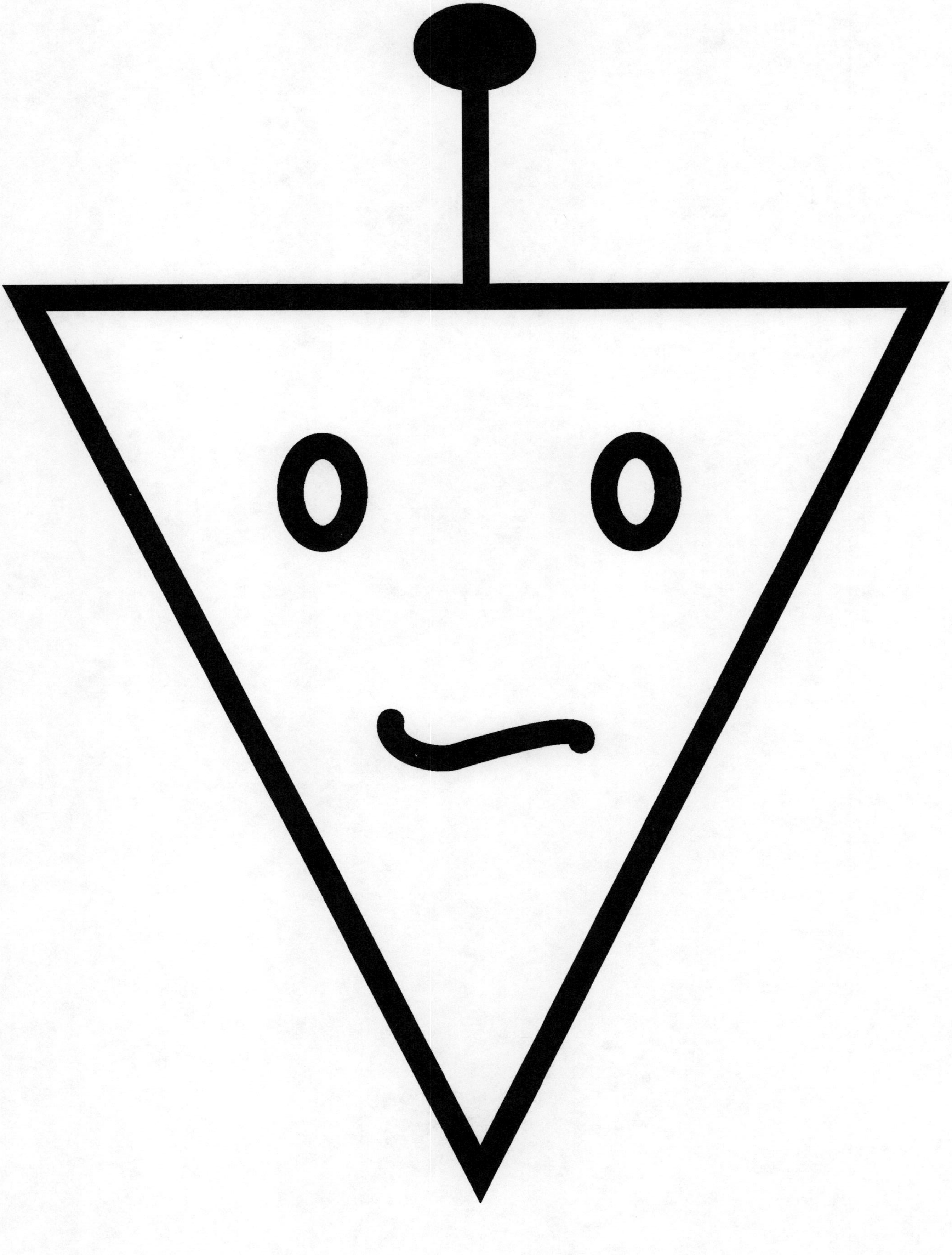

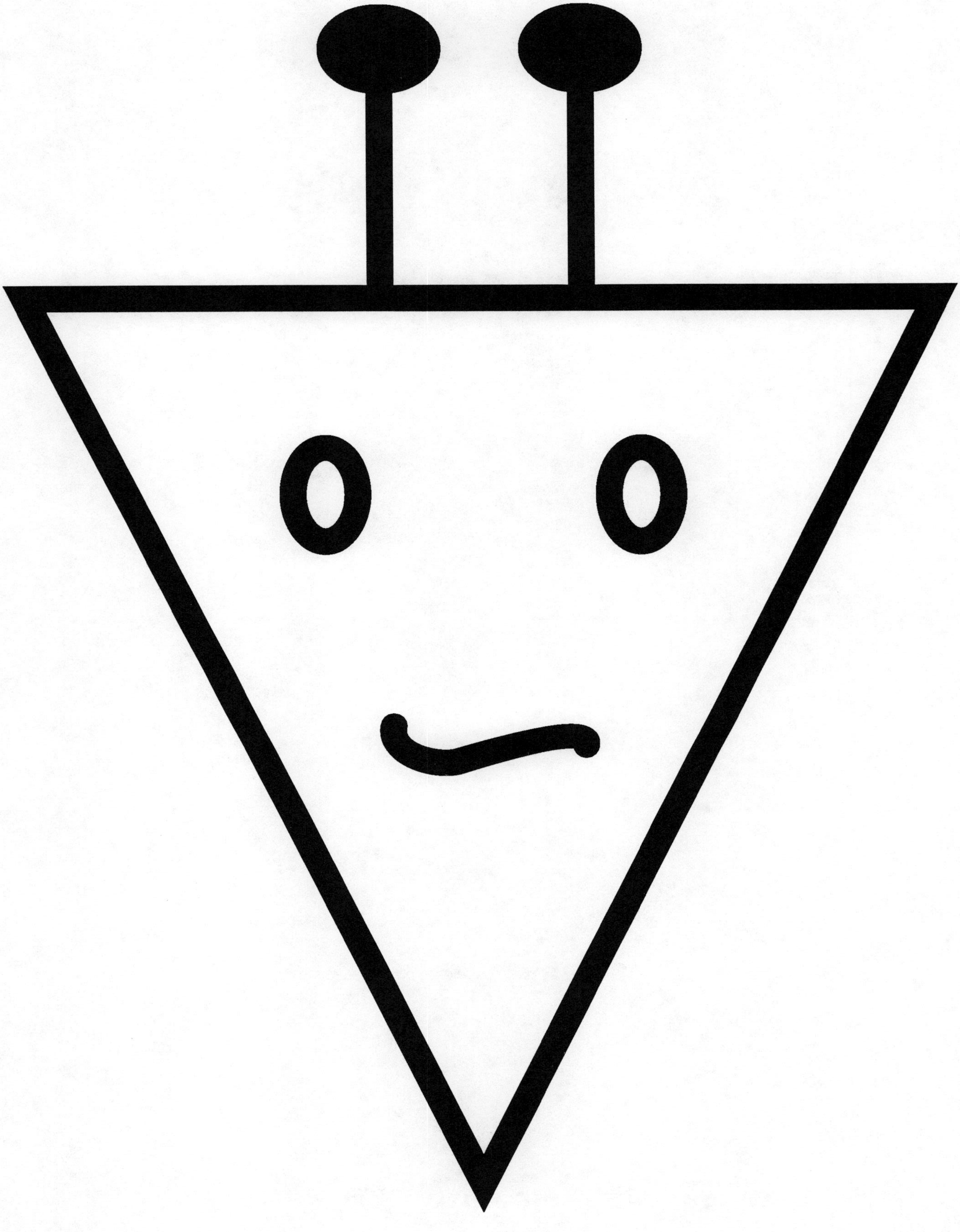

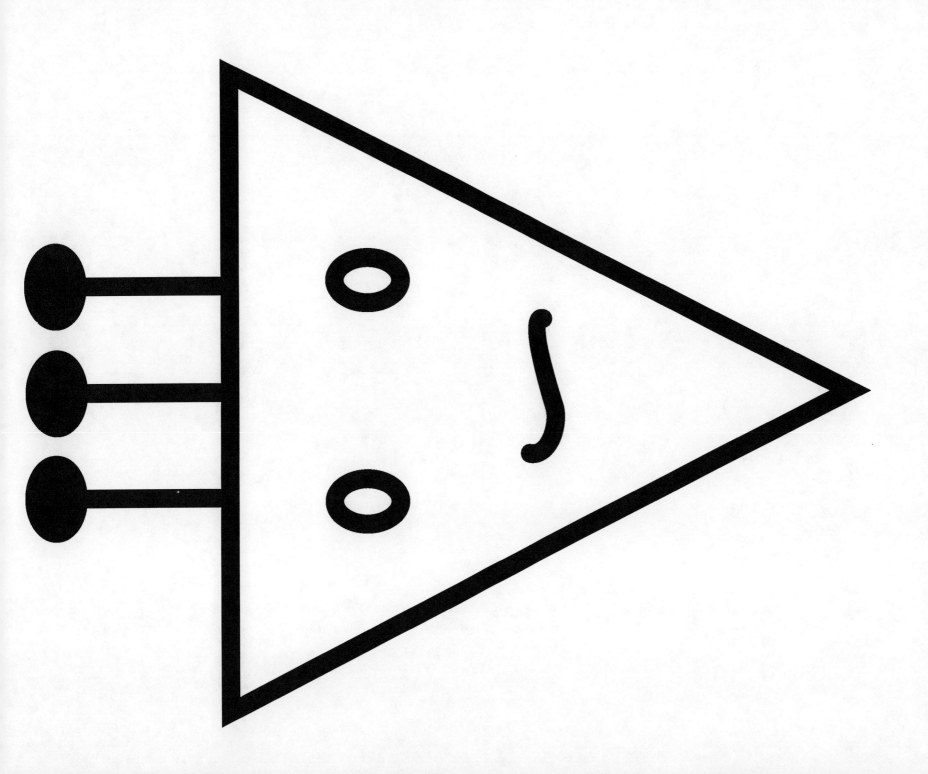

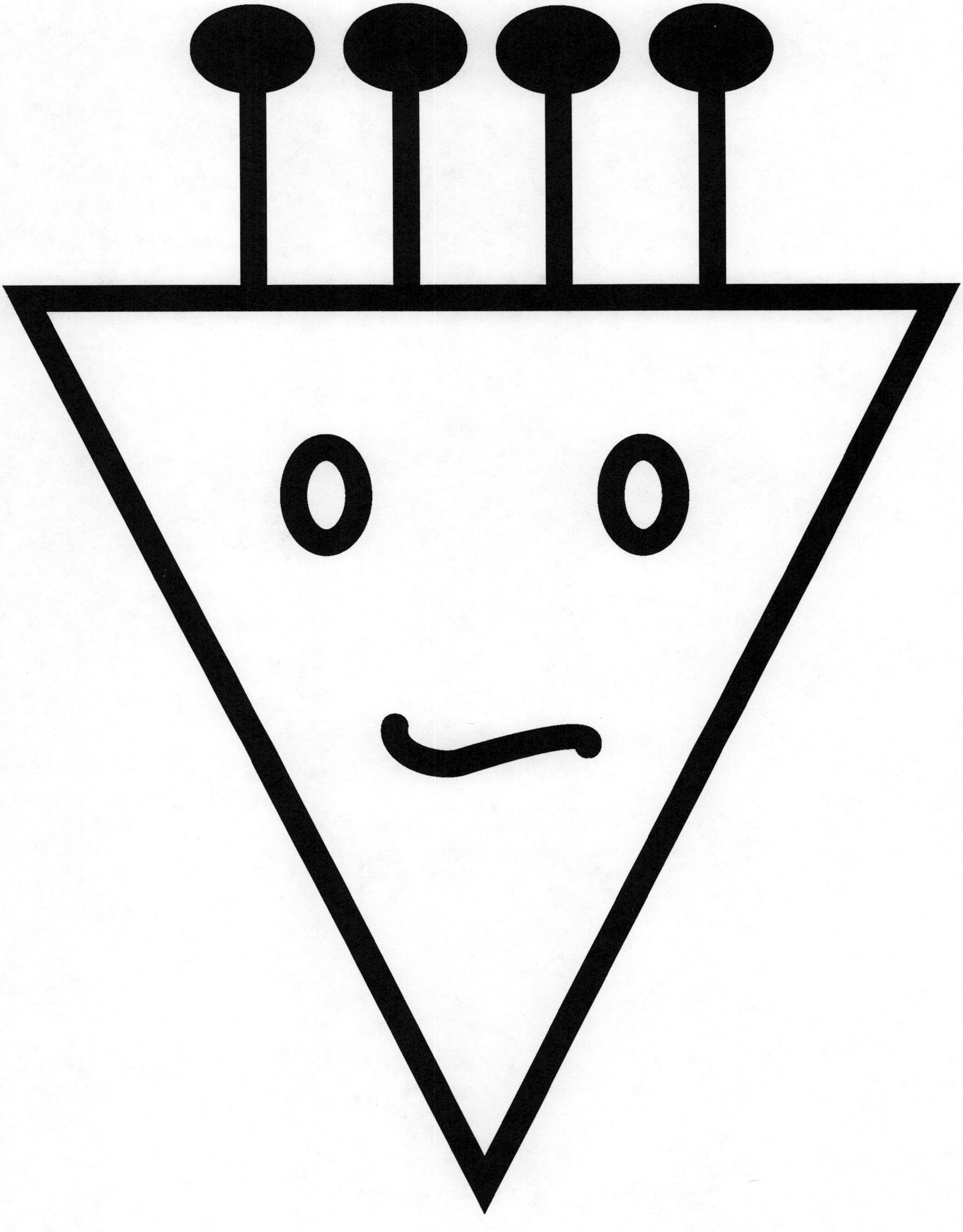

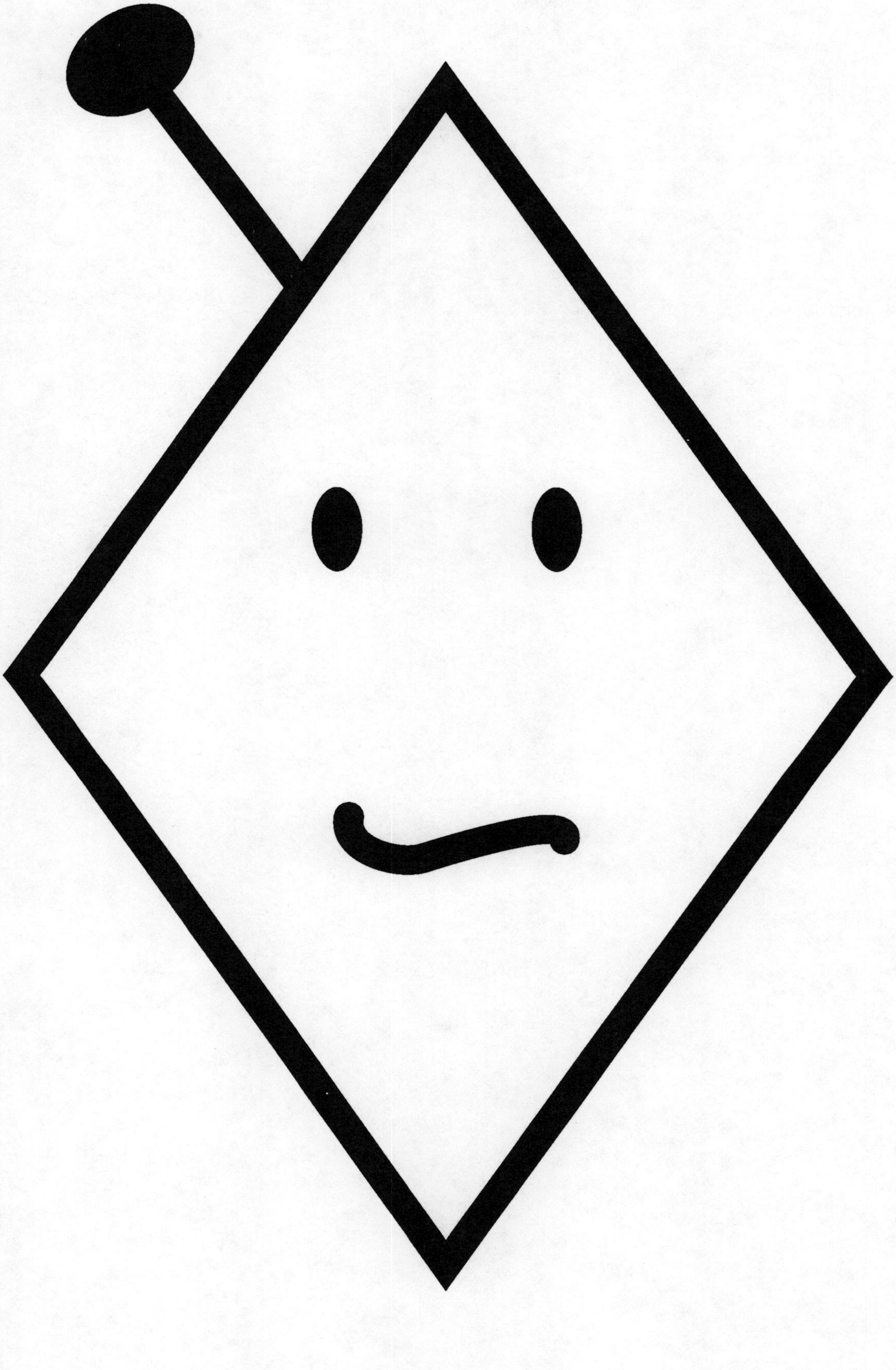

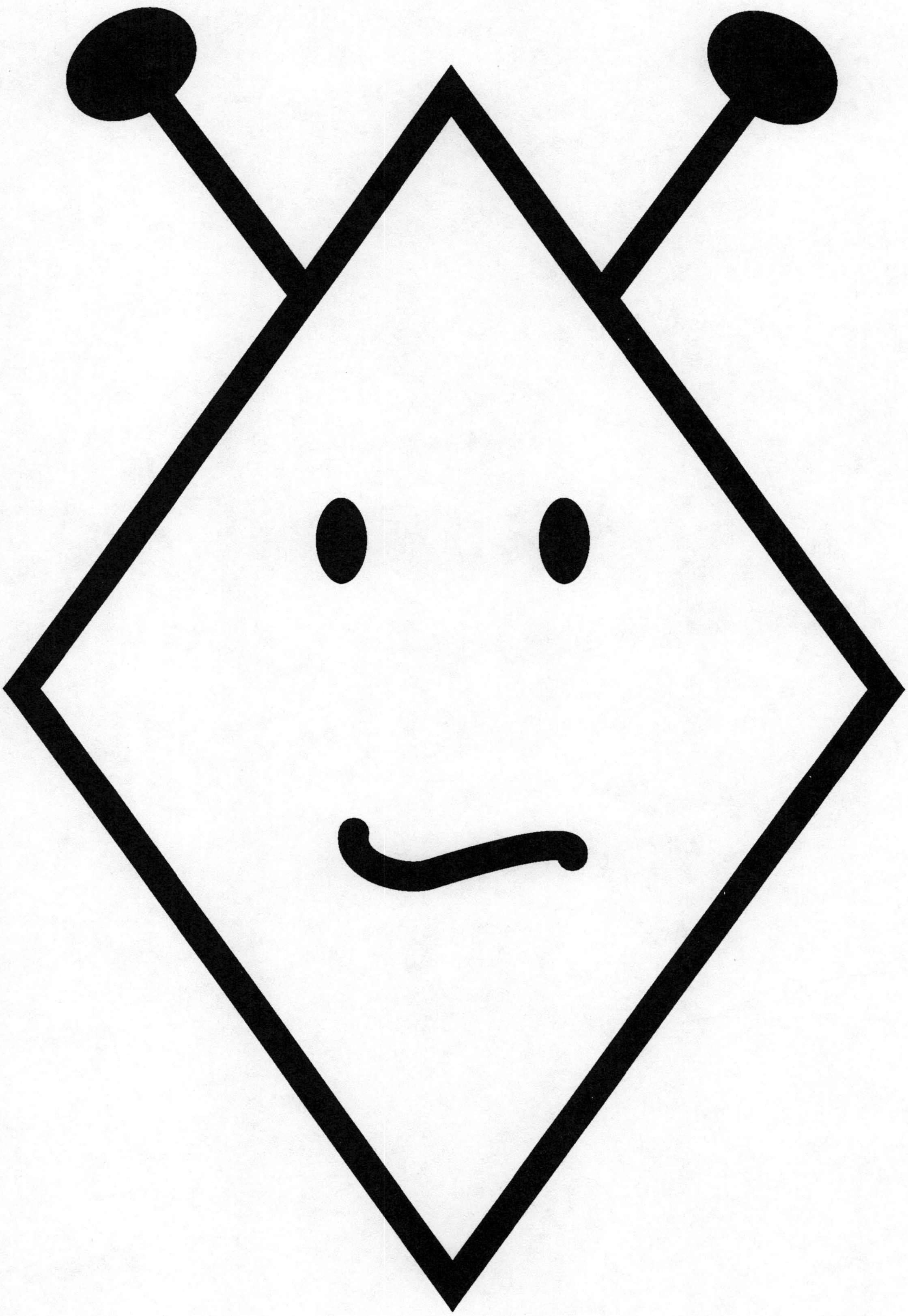

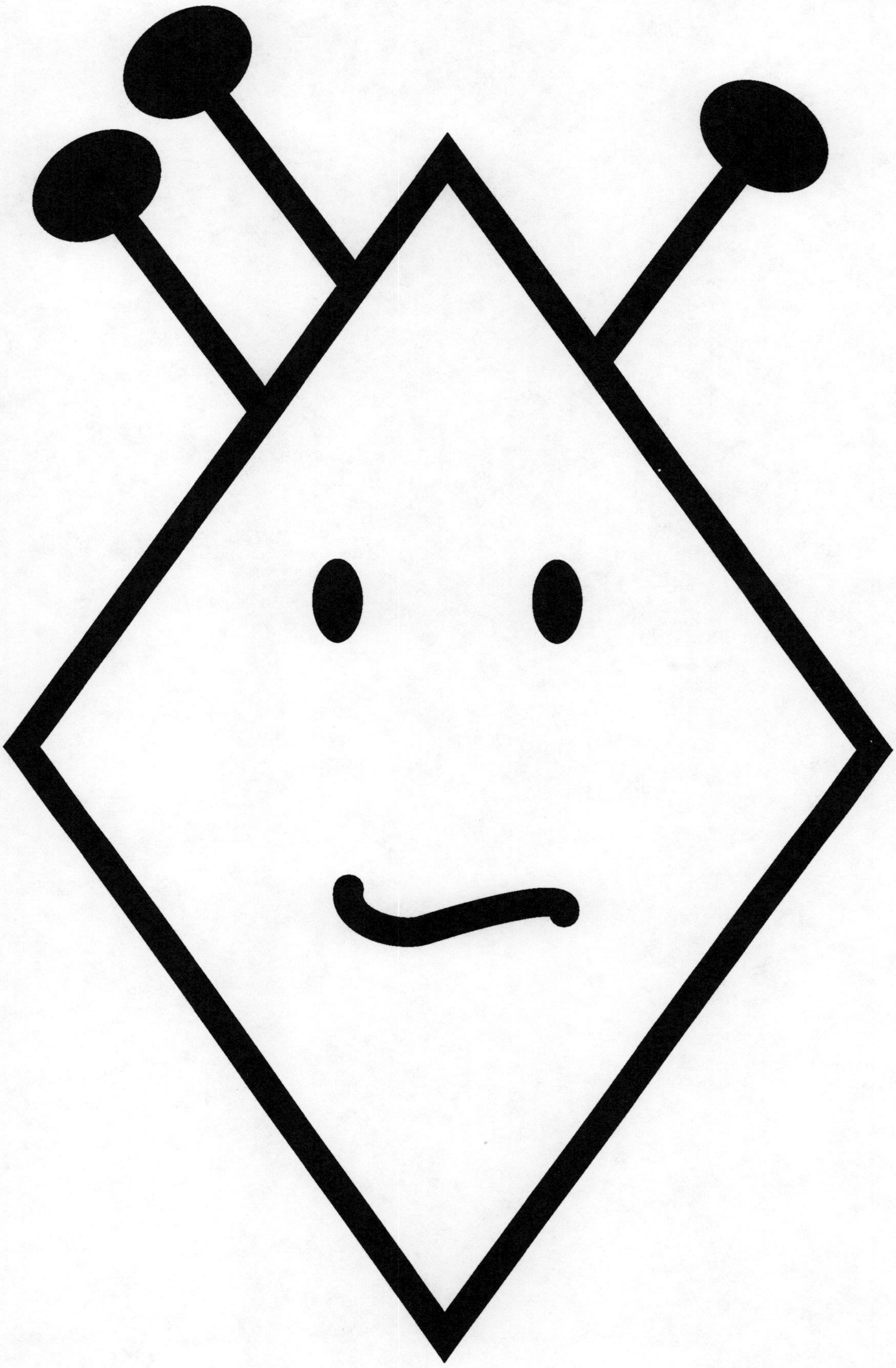

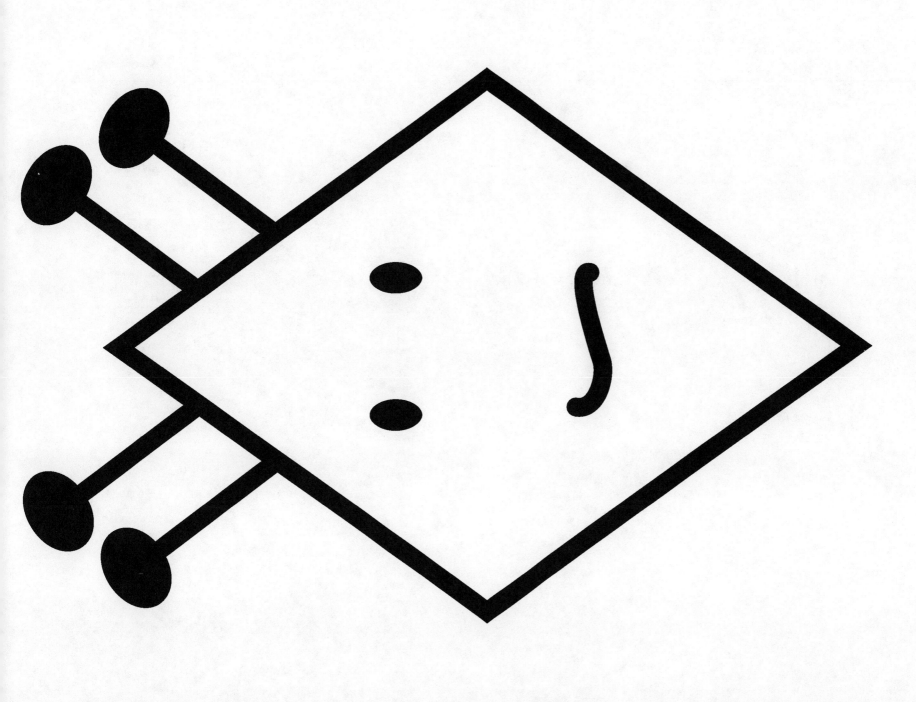

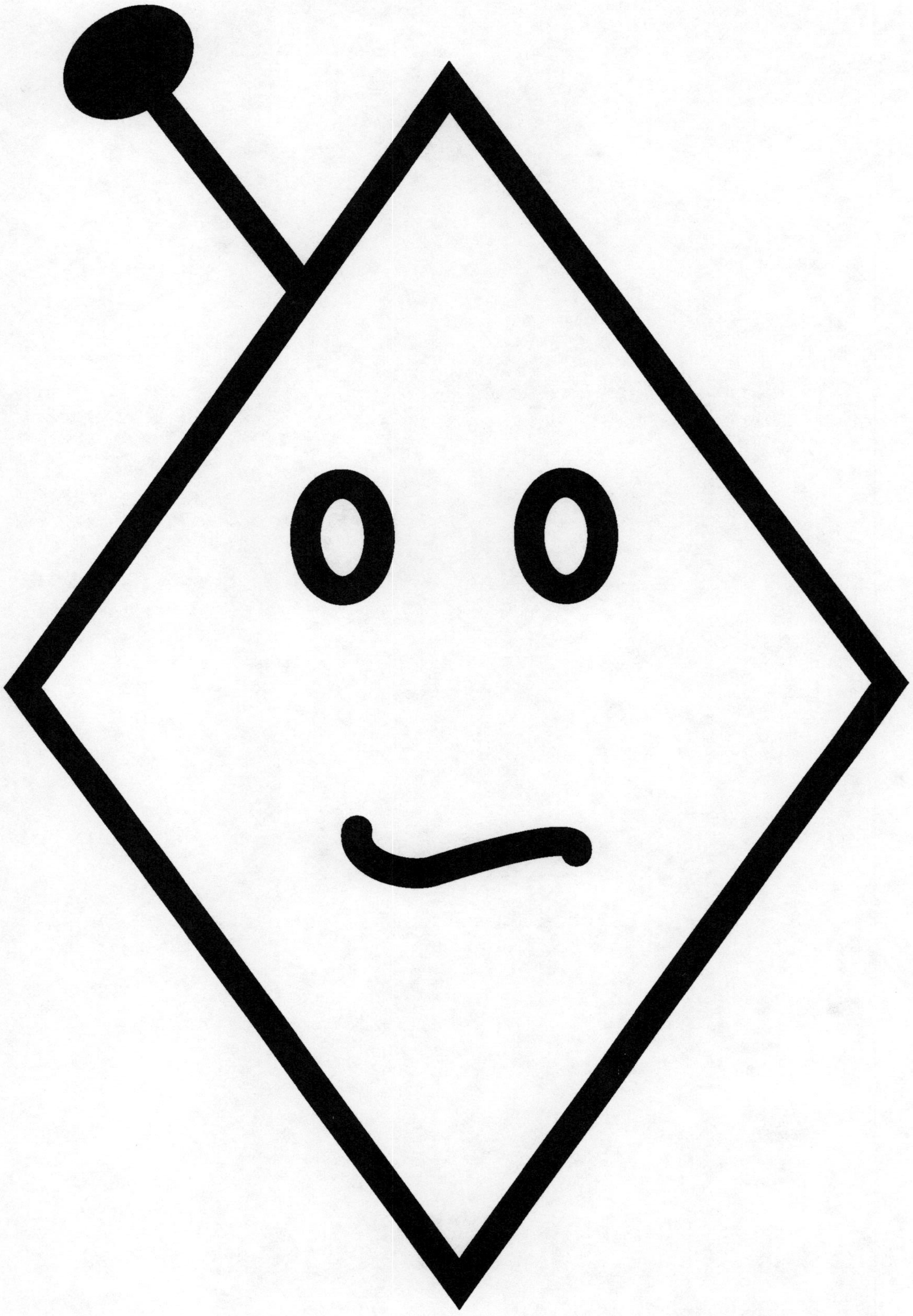

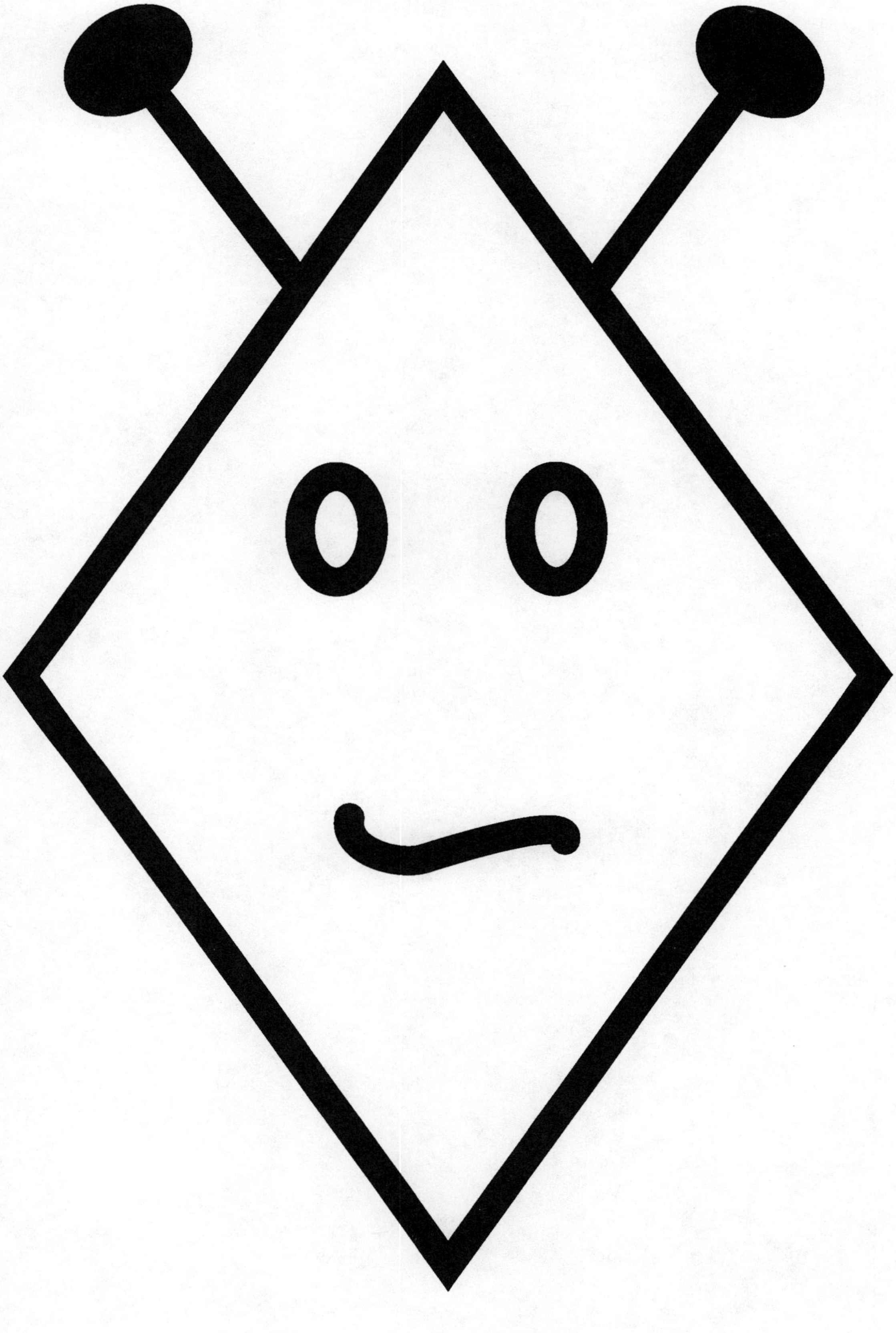

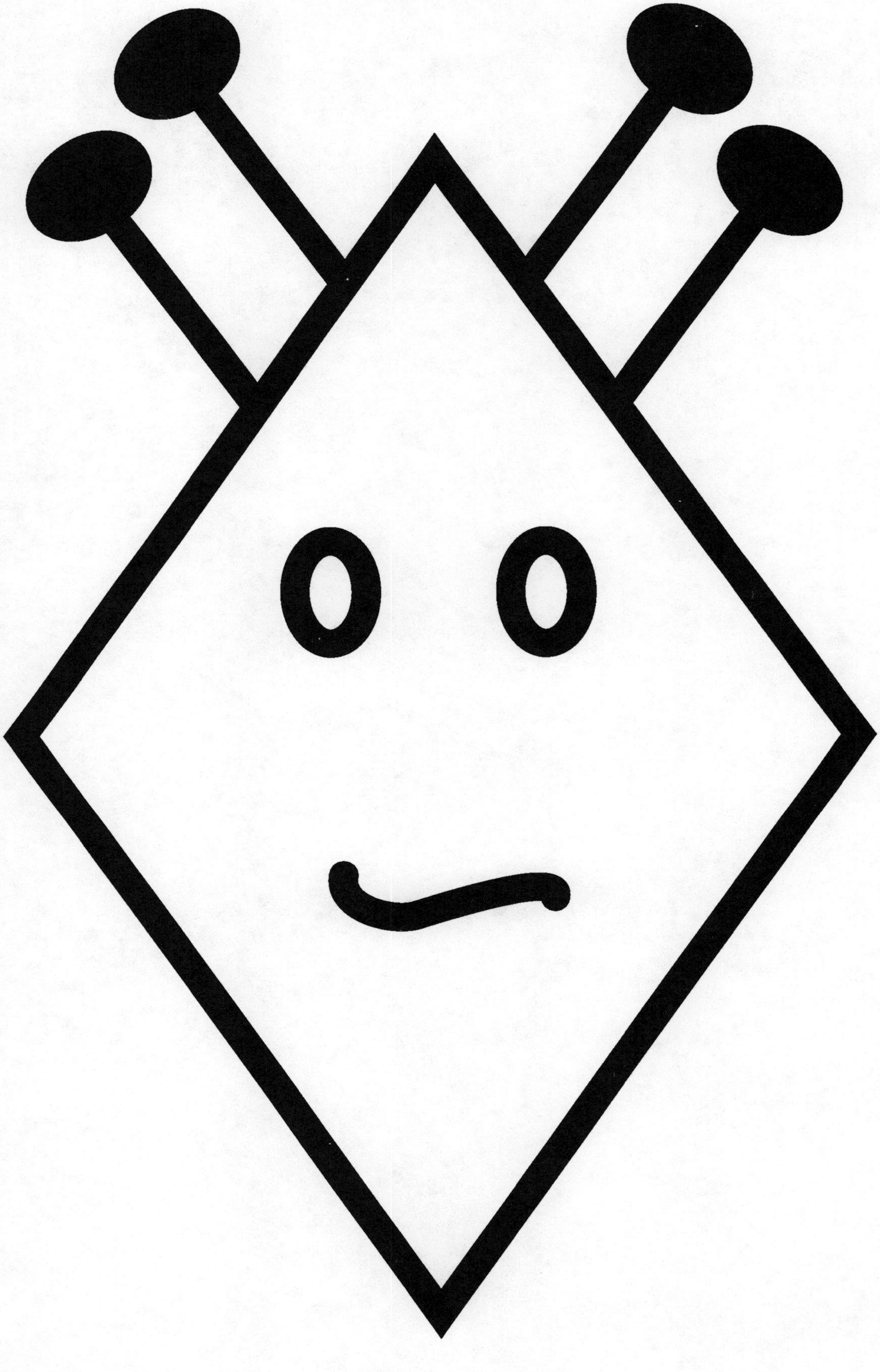

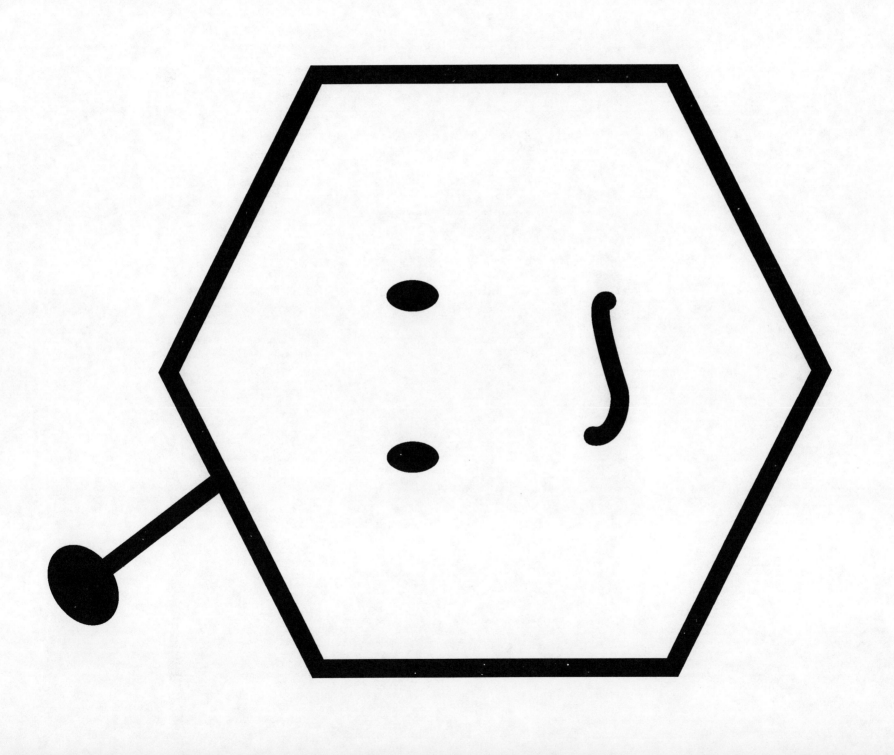

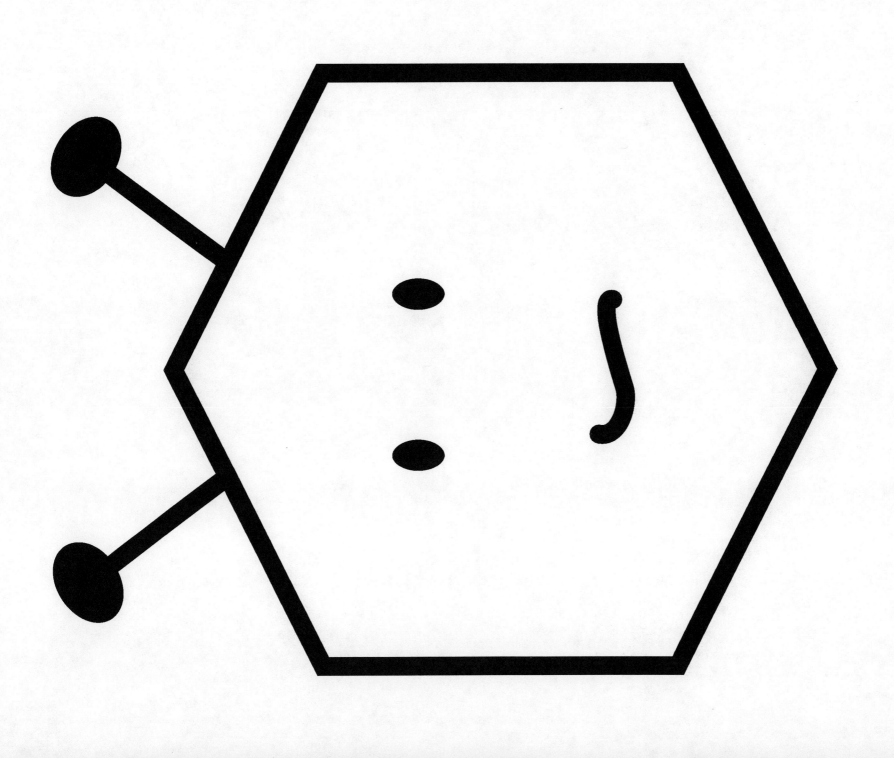

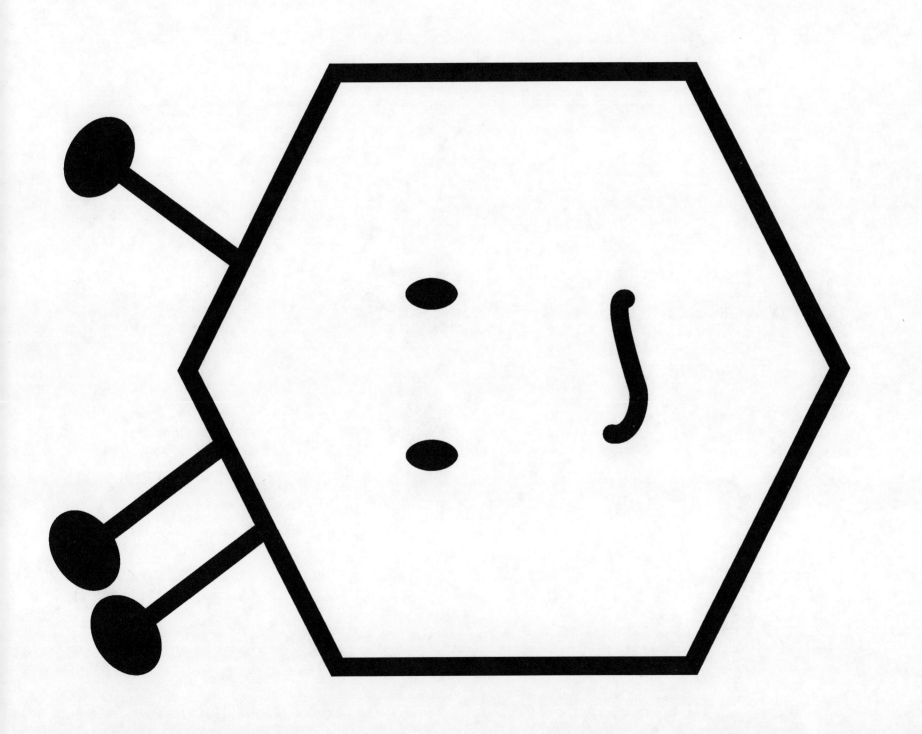

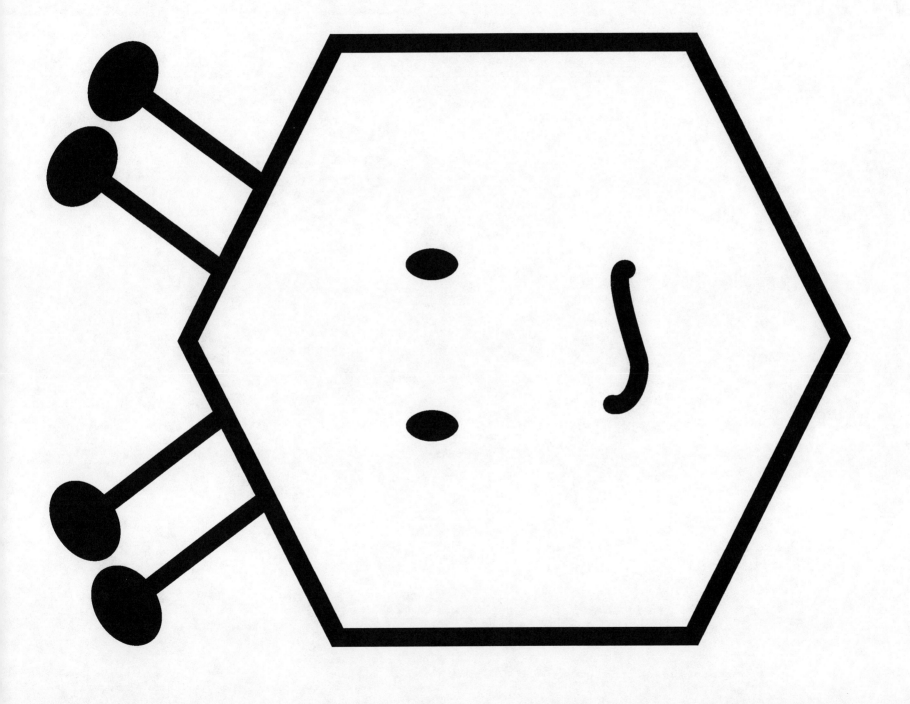

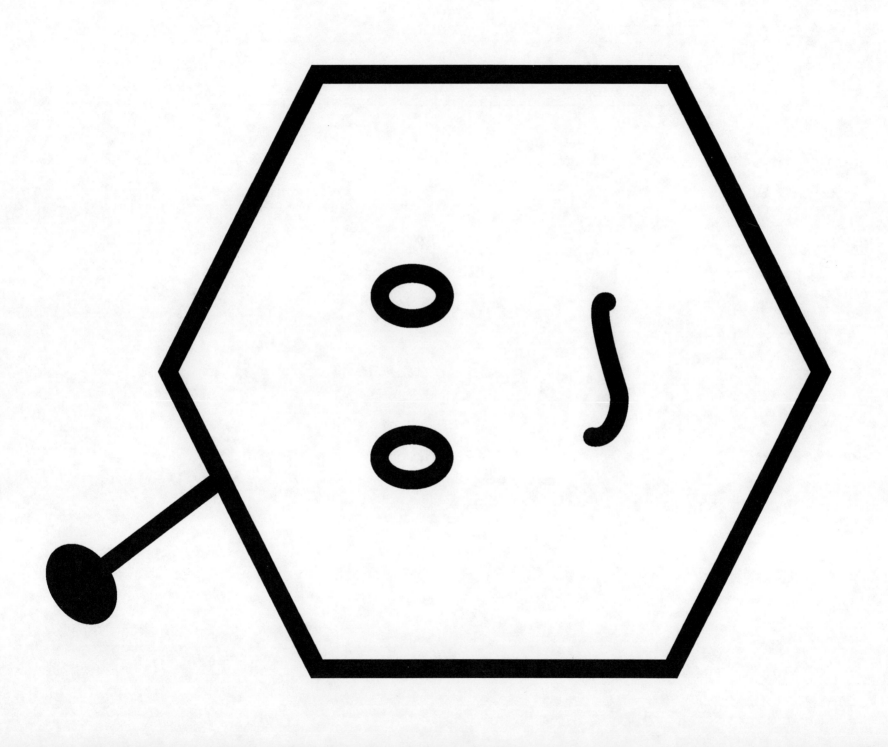

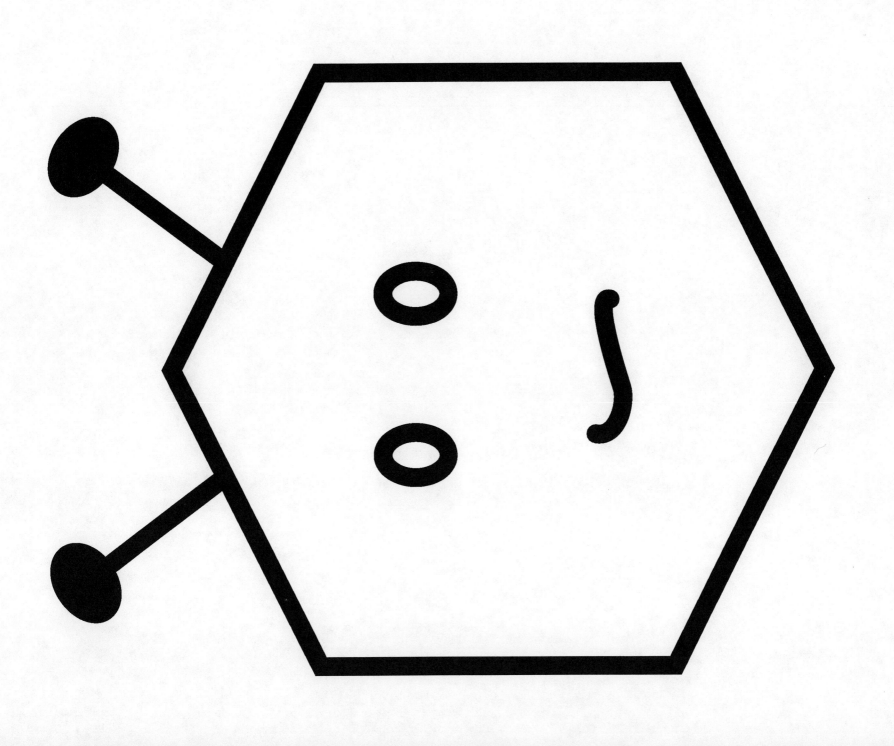

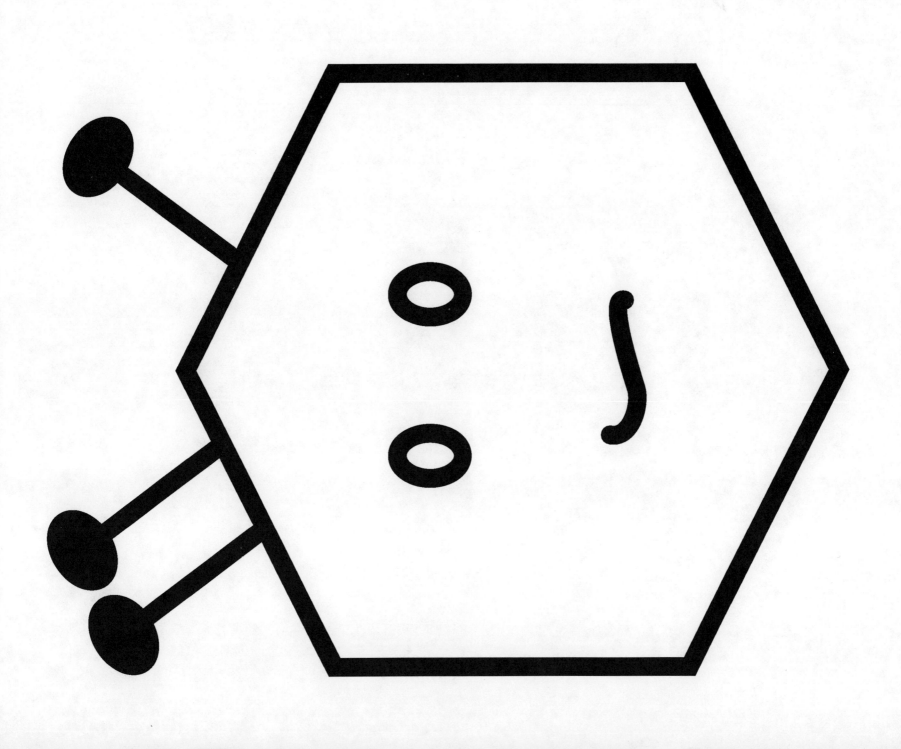

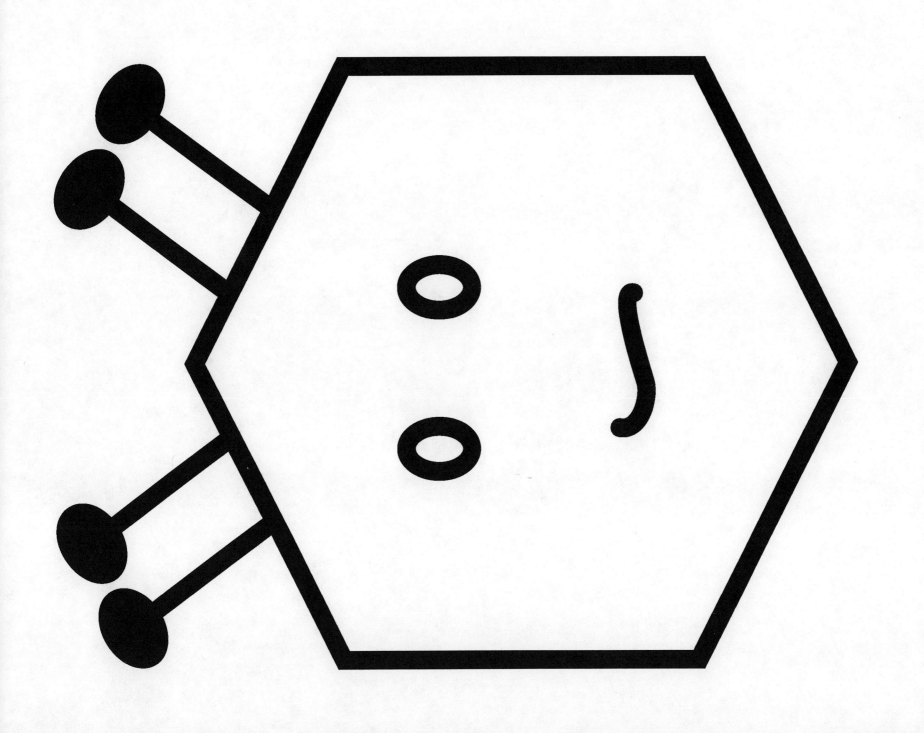